R U

Barents
Sea

FINLAND

POLAND

S W E D E N

GERMANY

N O R W A Y

North
Sea

FRANCE

ENGLAND

75°

65°

45°

G R E E N L A N D

Davis Strait

The FROZEN NORTH

A T L A N T I C

O C E A N

Hudson St.

LABRADOR

Miles

0   200   400   600

Morgan

PETER FREUCHEN, the late Danish explorer, understood the Eskimo and other inhabitants of the Far North better than any other man of our generation. Through his writings of his experiences and adventures during many long expeditions into the arctic, he has provided the world with knowledge, heretofore scant and inaccurate, about this mysterious society. The excitement and adventure of his world-renowned journeys come vividly to life within the pages of this gripping and colorful new book. Freuchen was a natural-born storyteller who could mesmerize an audience of any age group for hours with his fascinating yarns. His fervent interest in people, his amazing insight into human nature, and his intimate knowledge of the ways of the men of the north are communicated in every tale he tells.

Freuchen loved to travel and meet and make friends. He was able to teach and to help the people he met immeasurably. Yet he, too, learned a great many things from them about the human condition. Writing here of people from one end of the arctic to the other, he sympathetically tells of Moba, the submissive Alaskan wife; and Guolna, the hungry Lapp—two victims of circumstance. Satumen, an ex-prisoner who fled to the arctic; the Lapp Isak and his four star-crossed sons; Pekka, the Finnish widow; and Dr. Copp whose glass eye saw everything are just a few of the interesting and little-known people of

(continued on back flap)

Peter Freuchen's

MEN OF THE FROZEN NORTH

Peter Freuchen's

MEN OF

Cleveland and New York

THE FROZEN NORTH

EDITED AND WITH A PREFACE BY

DAGMAR FREUCHEN

THE WORLD PUBLISHING COMPANY

Published by *The World Publishing Company*
2231 West 110th Street, Cleveland 2, Ohio

Published simultaneously in Canada by
Nelson, Foster & Scott Ltd.

Library of Congress Catalog Card Number: 62-13946

FIRST EDITION

Drawings by Dagmar Freuchen

WP962

To the one man who meant more to me
than any other man in my whole life—

KNUD RASMUSSEN

Contents

CONTENTS

Illustrations

(Following Page 100)

ILLUSTRATIONS

Preface

THE TRUE MEASURE of Peter Freuchen's greatness as a
man was the overwhelming sense of joy and enthusiasm
that enveloped him every place he went. To him people
were not simply good or bad, useful or useless, pleasant
or unpleasant. They were above all *persons*. I do not mean
to say that he loved everybody (who does?), but he had a
sense of respect and reverence that gave him a boundless
interest in each person he met, whether he liked him
or not.

This quality of Peter's comes out, I believe, in a special
way in this book. He searches out the good things in the
people he met from one end of the arctic to the other.
And in some cases he had to search pretty deeply. But he
always came up with something—his observations are always full of humor or humanity or the pathos of the
human condition. Perhaps this is why Therkel Mathiassen
wrote that on the Fifth Thule Expedition Peter was
largely responsible for the good atmosphere among the
members—he always buoyed everyone up with his good
spirits and his optimism that things would turn out well
in the end.

Peter's unselfish love made itself particularly felt in his

13

concern for those who were "up against it." When, for instance, he learned that a friend of his had Parkinson's disease he wrote to him two or three times weekly for several years. And he wrote just as regularly to many others, sometimes sending presents to those he knew were sick or in some way underprivileged, never expecting an answer or even thanks. Frequently I meet people who tell me how much a letter from Peter meant on such or such an occasion.

One example comes immediately to my mind. When some people in Hollywood heard that Peter had escaped to Sweden from Nazi-occupied Denmark, they sent him money to help him through the difficult times. But Peter never spent a penny of their marvelous gift on himself. He used it all to help others less fortunate than himself, and aided many to escape from Denmark. I still hear stories about his wonderful generosity.

I mention these things because they give an insight to the stories in this book—stories like "Strube" or "Moba and Charley Jim." Only a man like Peter could probe so deeply into the cruelties and tragic elements of fate and turn up positive, redemptive qualities in these characters. Such discoveries are essential, but how many writers find it impossible to make them!

Such discoveries, I believe, were also the springboard for Peter's talent as a storyteller. Where he ever developed his unique talent for telling stories in such a gripping way, I do not know. It may have been the result of those long dark evenings with the Eskimos during snowstorms. Time went by more quickly, no doubt, when good stories were told. Perhaps, too, this is why his stories have such simplicity. Things seem to take place right in front of your eyes.

Everywhere Peter went, people loved to hear his stories. They never seemed to have enough. One evening, when we lived in Noank, Connecticut, our weekend guests arrived tired from their drive from New York and wanted to go right to bed. While we were standing around, saying good night, Peter started telling stories. He kept on and on, and the guests forgot how tired they were. We stayed up almost till dawn.

Children, particularly, loved to listen to Peter's stories, and he loved to talk to them—mostly, I think, because he liked unsophisticated people. Once, on an island in the Caribbean, Peter went to take a swim. When I joined him a few minutes later, he was surrounded by children of all ages and shapes; listening in spellbound silence, they wouldn't miss a word of his tales.

Peter was naturally happy to see how people liked what he had to say, and so was I. I still rejoice over the welcome reception that is given to every one of Peter's books—it must be that he touches something that people feel dearly in their hearts, that his concern releases a sense of sympathy people feel the need to release. Albert Lewin wrote that the first time he saw Peter was outside a Hollywood studio on a blistering hot day; Peter, he said, was holding something in his hands, protecting it. Al approached and saw that Peter had a little bird with a broken wing. Peter said he had seen the bird hopping helplessly around and wanted to take care of it until it was well and could fly again. This event, I feel, speaks volumes about Peter's character; it was a symbol of his attitude to suffering humanity, the way he dealt with men and described them to others.

You will find all these qualities of Peter in this new book. It was a work of love for me to edit it—one of the most deeply rewarding experiences of my life.

DAGMAR FREUCHEN

New York,
February 18, 1962

THE INDIANS
OF ALASKA
AND
NORTHERN
CANADA

I.

How I Got To Know the Northern Indians

I ONCE SPENT a whole year in Alaska with a movie company and had the opportunity to travel all over *free of charge*. This, which must be one of the most generous things ever done by any industry any place in the world, also provided me with some of the happiest memories of my life. I used to wander up and down the inland waterways of Alaska, and stop whenever I cared to. Sometimes I came as far south as Oregon and once made northwestern California. I even made a trip into the arctic basin occupied by Eskimos, one of the richest hunting grounds in the world, and also one of the most beautiful and startling, since great spruce forests and great riverways come upon the traveler suddenly, like ghosts in the night.

But my main concern in all these trips was to get acquainted with the Indians of the north—the Tlingit, Haida, Tsimshian Indians of the northernmost tundra, the Kwakiutl of the Milbanke-Queen Charlotte region, and the coast Salish who occupy the Straits of Georgia and Puget Sound. I wasn't a scientist digging up ruins or an engineer building bridges or a prospector looking for gold. I just wanted to see people, find out how they lived, and discover man's condition in a place I had not previously seen.

I was very fortunate in that the director of the picture was Colonel W. S. Van Dyke, the well-known American traveler and author. Colonel Van Dyke was an exceptional man and a brilliant scholar. He had deep inner resources which I greatly admired, and I was happy to talk with him, or to travel with him when I had the chance, since I always came away richer. He had a way of saying the most profound things, as if he stood apart from reality in seeing it and then plunged back into it when his analysis was completed.

We were sitting one day in the famous city of Nome at Norton Sound, enjoying a delicious meal of big crabs known all over the world as "Japanese crabs" even though they came from Alaskan waters. The Colonel expressed his astonishment that the Alaskans themselves didn't put these crabs in cans rather than let the Japanese do it. "This," he remarked, "is enough to start a war."

I was amazed to hear the Colonel say this, since I didn't believe anyone would want to die for crabs. And I told him so.

"It isn't just for the crabs," the Colonel said. "The crabs can be taken only in wintertime when the Eskimos can get out on the ice with their sledges. To take them at any other time of the year a man has to go more than three miles out to sea, since the waters are very shallow around here. But the Japanese schooners are all out there and they won't let the Americans or any Eskimos take part in the catch. Nothing of course can be proved. But

the fishermen don't dare to go out there. They just disappear, they never come back."

"Why not let them take the crabs?" I asked. "They taste
the same to me whether they're Japanese or Alaskan."
Being a Dane I could not share the Colonel's patriotism
over the crabs.

"Japan is enjoying American waters without any brakes
put on them," the Colonel explained. "Nothing is done
to protect Alaska. There are only two hundred soldiers
here—no guns, no nothing. But mark my words—some day
we will want the waters, the crabs, and everything. And
when we do, Japan will start a war."

Years later, back in Denmark, I remembered the Colonel's statement. Strange as it seemed in 1927, it left me
thunderstruck when remembering it on December 7,
1941.

That was the sort of man Colonel Van Dyke was. No
one could understand completely what he meant until
it was too late.

But I somehow realized even when I first met Colonel
Van Dyke that there was more to his words than just
struck the ear. That is why I always paid the closest attention to anything he said about the Indians. I wanted to
get to know the Indians while I was in Alaska in the same
manner that I knew the Eskimos with whom I had lived
since 1909.

"You will notice," said the Colonel, giving me my first
lesson about the Indians, "that the sea resources appear
more stripped in this northwest portion of America than
in any place north of Mexico. That is because the greatest
prehistoric population lived right here. They lived on

fish, sea mammals, shellfish, seaweed, and even birds that feed on the sea. And they used this food to such an extent that nature hasn't recovered yet. The signs of their visit are still evident. Perhaps they always will be. They also used the cedar, making houses and boats and boxes out of it, even carving masks and objects of worship from it.

"This," continued the Colonel, "is why we guess that peoples must have migrated this way from Asia. It is not only the easiest way to come, but also the one that provided the best food in the easiest way. So the large bulk of people must have first stopped here, then split up into their various routes. They were like water flowing through the neck of a bottle."

I marveled that the Colonel had figured things out so closely, but the results of my countrywide trips only bore out what he said. Years later I passed the speculation on to some professor, and now it is to be found in every textbook. That, I hope, isn't always the way of academic learning, for stray bits of information might not always have as good a source as Colonel Van Dyke.

Once, on a trip to the interior with the Colonel, we stopped to watch an Indian weaving a basket. "Would you believe that those fine threads are made from bark fiber?" he asked. I bent over the basket, looking at the thread closely. It was hardly the width of a hair.

"It seems almost woolen," I said.

"There is some wool in it," the Colonel told me. "The wool of mountain goats is combined with the inner bark of spruce or cypress and spun in an ancient way to make this yarn. The Indian follows an ancient technique, but one that varies from tribe to tribe and place to place. The baskets are different in almost every tribe, every group. On that basis scientists have guessed that the people came from a number of different places in Asia—perhaps as many as fifty."

The story of world migration was beginning to fit together very simply in the Colonel's apt stories and images, together with his knowledge of archaeology. I was glad I was with him.

With this start in archaelogy, I began to figure out some things about the Indian for myself. One that interested me very much was the ceremony of the Potlatch, or Potlasch, as it is sometimes called, in which an individual's or tribe's wealth is squandered to get public standing. Perhaps this was the most difficult of all the problems I set for myself. Why, I wondered, should people throw away the meager possessions they have just to impress people? The "big shot" theory, according to which a man becomes great by blowing his friends to a treat, satisfies most archaeologists; but it didn't satisfy me. I thought of many different things, but one day I asked Colonel Van Dyke what he thought.

"There was a fellow I knew in Brooklyn," he began. "He went bankrupt every once in a while no matter how hard he worked. But just when he got down to a hundred dollars, he called it quits, then brought all his friends in and threw a big party, after which everyone traveled all over Manhattan in cabs. He wasn't trying to be a big shot. He wanted to make a final stand against what he considered a hostile economic universe. And I think the Indians do the same thing with regard to the physical universe."

That explanation was a lot more genuine as far as I was concerned. As a matter of fact, I have applied it two or three times in my own life, when things were getting pretty low.

I loved to travel around and meet the Indians. They are possessed of a folklore and religious imagery that is among the richest in the world. I have always thought it a pity that scientists should spend so much time discovering the origins of the Indian without paying more attention to their effects—their marvelous understanding of nature, of the dignity of an Indian chief and his braves.

And I always regretted that the Indians were legislated into reservations, put into a second-rate position, sold cheap liquor and guns, when they could have been made a part of society.

2.

Moba and Charley Jim

A TINY LITTLE GIRL. Such a pitiful little thing when she was born—but still she was tossed about as carelessly as any papoose. The first things she sensed were the howls of the dogs and a feeling of cold. Her first pain came from blows intended for her mother, but which also struck her, when the whip her father swung curled around her mother's body.

She could not remember her father. When he died was of no importance. She heard whispers that he had been rewarded, the time he had saved the white men from the forest fires down by Big Slave Lake. And again she heard that he had been punished for helping to bring the white man's firewater into their country to be sold. When she grew bigger, she ran around and played when there was peace in the village, but soon learned to stay hidden away when the men came home. There was always trouble in the air at those times.

Her mother was old and worn out. Her ragged clothes could not keep her undernourished body warm. But she was so good! She never ate a bite of meat before Moba had had more than she wanted, even though what was left was not always enough. But one day the mother lay gasping and breathing so strangely. She was hot, and her face shone, and she said never a word when Moba came in from her play. The little girl soon forgot all this and went into the other tents where the men had just made a catch, and where there was enough meat so that she might eat all she wanted, without anyone else being deprived of food.

That night she returned to her mother's tent. She found two of the nuns from the mission there. Moba saw that her mother lay very still and that she hardly seemed to breathe. Then the two nuns washed Moba. *That* wasn't so pleasant! But afterward they gave her wonderful food, and later, when she had slept for a time, the two women woke her, and said many strange words. They sang their strange songs. Then they told Moba that she was to go home with them, for now she no longer had a mother.

Next morning the little girl awoke in a fine bed. It was white and clean, and the nuns in the house all spoke kindly to her. Some spoke to her smilingly—others were cold, with severe-looking mouths. But all were kind, and she was given plenty of food, and new clothes. She was even allowed to look at the lovely pictures in the big books.

Moba stayed with the nuns. Soon it seemed as though she had always lived with them. She went to school with the other Indian children and learned to read. She also learned the foreign language spoken by the nuns, and found it easy to remember everything she had been taught. Often it seemed as though the other children had dull brains, or that there was no way to reach their brains, for they soon forgot all they learned. But Moba didn't forget.

When school was over, the children played until a bell rang, whereupon the Indian children went home to their own tents. Moba went indoors and ate fine food, the kind that must be eaten with a spoon. When she was given meat, she was told that it was a disgrace to hold it with her hands. She was given a fork to stick into her meat, and she had to cut it into pieces.

In this way the little Moba learned bit by bit to look upon everything the nuns did as the right thing. Once in a while she longed to be with her own folk again. This she told the Prioress, and occasionally was given permission to accompany Sister Therese when she brought food to the sick, or for other reasons visited the tent village. Then Moba could run about and play as she liked. She noticed at those times how the Indians seemed to have forgotten that she was a little orphan. They treated her like a real person! They talked kindly to her, gave her much food and luscious meat-bones, things that tasted quite different from the food the nuns ate, and was *much* more delicious.

She should never have mentioned this at home, but one day she spoke of it. The Prioress immediately said that it did Moba no good to visit her people, that these visits must stop. After that she was never permitted to go to the village.

One day she sobbed with longing for the comrades whom she saw only in school, and begged to be allowed to sleep down in the tents once in a while.

"You will get lice," said Sister Therese, "and they itch."

"Oh, no, they don't itch at all. It's nice, and it's lots of fun to find them when they crawl around on your body."

But Sister Therese said that was a poor way to talk, and

took her to Mother Madeleine. Mother told Moba that since she was so quick to learn, and had such a good brain to remember all she learned, it had been decided that Moba should sail with next summer's ship. She was going to travel down the great river to the landing place. From there she would ride in a great wagon—all closed up like a house—to the place where she would live and learn all the wise things the white men had discovered.

Moba's eyes grew big with wonder, and she became more and more curious as the day drew nearer for going on the ship. More clothes were sewed for her, and this made her very happy. The nuns told her she would like living with the new people. They had a place where she would learn about God, and become good—just as God wished her to be—and then later she could return home and tell her own people all she had learned. She could teach them to be good people, so that they would go to Heaven when they died.

Moba loved the hymns and all the wonderful things they told her about the Virgin Mary and the Christ Child. She thought much of them, and asked many questions about Heavenly things. Often the sisters found it difficult to answer her. But they always praised her understanding. And when the ship came, Moba knew they were sad at the thought of her departure. She too was sorry to leave, for she was afraid that Mother Madeleine might die before she returned. It might be many years, and Mother Madeleine was very old. She had been bedridden for the last few years.

But she soon forgot all her fears when she felt the ship's propeller move, and watched the land on both sides of the river slip past her. Endless forests—queer houses—and more forests and more houses.

Moba traveled with two sisters. They were grave but friendly. Moba noticed that their clothes were different from what people around them wore.

"Why don't you have beautiful clothes like the people who live here?" asked Moba. "Let us go into a store and buy some colored clothes."

But they told her they would not lay aside their black habits, and when she was grown up she too would wear black clothes, so that her thoughts might not be turned from God by things which would perish. Moba thought this was all very tiresome, and she made up her mind that when she was big enough to buy her own dresses, they'd be red and green and yellow.

There were many children at the school, and many small girls like Moba. They told her about their fathers and mothers and families. Moba understood that life was very different where they came from, and that they had been very happy in their homes. But they were not often permitted to talk of their homes. The good sisters arranged their play, decided what they should read, and saw to it that the children were always cheerful, that they always remembered how everybody must please God. Moba learned her prayers and responses, and was much praised for her sweet voice. When she knelt and thought of the divine goodness of the Heavenly Mother, she forgot all about herself.

Moba became capable and efficient at school. Every year there was an examination held at the school; the bishop, the abbot, and many priests came to hear how well the pupils had learned their lessons. For a long time before this, the children were nervous and afraid at the thought of the visiting pious men who were to come, but it always proved that there was no cause for fear, for the visitors were good and friendly. If there were those who had not studied as they should have done, they were rebuked and sternly advised to mend their ways. But this always happened in such a way that everybody felt it was for the culprit's own good. Moba had never been reproved. Once the bishop had laid his hand on her head and gently patted her. He said she would prove to be a blessing to her people.

Taller and taller she grew, and the days and the years went by and she learned more and more. She was so clever in all her studies that she was not sent away from the school like some of the others, but remained there for further study, until at last she received the degree of Master of Arts in languages. But she never forgot her own native tongue.

Later on, she studied with a learned priest. After some time, she took her final examinations and got high honors. All praised her and said God showed His goodness in endowing one of the poor northern folk with cleverness and understanding. So now she was to return home and become a teacher to her own people.

Moba sailed up the river. This time there were others in the party. She still remembered Sister Therese and Mother Madeleine, but there were so many others whom she had learned to know, and she had studied so much, that her head seemed empty of old memories. She traveled in the bishop's party. He was on his way to visit the good sisters on the Mackenzie River. They lived in the Far North to serve God and to spread His gospel among the poor miserable Indians.

The ship's crew was a rough lot, using many ugly words, which everybody tried to keep from Moba's ears. She, however, felt that these words were amusing and far different from those she had learned in the convent.

Now the ship lay to. She knew the place and she knew the houses again. And there was Sister Therese! The others from the mission were strangers to her, but they all looked happy as they greeted the bishop and his party. And when they saw Moba, they called aloud in their pleasure at seeing her. Everybody went to the mission house together, but when they arrived at the gate, the bishop struck his hands together, exclaiming:

"I was so glad to see you all, and so busy talking, that I forgot my little bag. I hope the ship hasn't sailed yet. Moba, you run down and get my bag. It's in my cabin, just inside the door."

She ran as fast as her long dress would permit. It seemed as if her legs knew how delightful it was to run on one's native heath again.

The others entered the mission house, and sat down to eat together. Everybody was so glad to see the bishop. They spoke together for a long time. Then they wondered why Moba did not return.

When they had waited another hour, they became uneasy, but thought she hadn't been able to find the bishop's bag. But after a little while longer, they went down to inquire about her, and found that the ship had sailed.

But Moba was not aboard, was she?

No, they told them.

But where was she?

She had come for the bag and had gone ashore again.

Someone had seen her talking with one of her own tribe. There was a Northwest Mounted Police station in the village, but the bishop did not want the law to interest itself in the matter. Two of the nuns were told to go to the Indian tents and get Moba. They were to tell her that it was right for her to seek her own people. But it was *not* right to do this until she had talked with the bishop and learned in what way he thought it best for her to meet her people again.

After a while the messengers returned, frightened. No one had seen Moba, no one knew where she was.

So now the bishop went to the old police sergeant and asked his help. Soon an old Indian cook admitted that Moba had gone away with Charley Jim, but that—he said—was all *he* knew about the matter.

Charley Jim was a rascal who drifted from one trading post to another. At times he was a beggar. If he chose to work, he could be a good worker for a short time, but would suddenly leave his tasks and go hunting. He'd be gone a while and then come back with the finest of furs, which he sold for a good price. He'd carouse until his money was gone, and then he'd drift again until a new fit took him to do a little work. But now Charley Jim had vanished, taking Moba with him.

Time passed. The bishop had returned home from his visit of inspection. At the mission house, the nuns had become resigned to the thought that Moba, the young and clever teacher who had won all the school prizes, and who had stood highest in the examinations, was gone.

Suddenly one day Moba came running to them. The

sisters heard a pounding on the door in the hall, and like a whirlwind, Moba rushed in.

"Save me—save me—he'll kill me!"

They saw Charley Jim at her heels.

The Prioress rose and walked to the door to meet the frenzied Indian.

"Go out," she said. "Let this woman alone. This house is closed to you."

And her commanding look and calm face forced him to obey. He had lifted his hand to strike or to push her aside, but she stood there so straight—so unafraid—stretching out her arm—

"Go," she said again. So he spat out curses in that strange, unintelligible Indian tongue that sounds like a whisper of consonants, and went, leaving Moba alone with the nuns.

"Little Moba," said the Prioress, patting her head—without a rebuking word. All the good sisters cared about was to have her safe with them, and to make her understand that they wished only her good.

She was half-starved, and her clothes were tattered. She looked worn-out; one could hardly believe it had been only three weeks and not years that she had toiled and slaved.

When she was clothed decently again, and sat talking quietly with the Prioress, her tears rose to the surface, and Moba became again the little girl who sat before the good mother superior, receiving both comfort and admonishments.

It appeared that the bishop's bag was safe. Moba had kept it from Charley Jim. She had asked him to let her return it, and here she was. Little by little they heard from her what had happened. But it didn't explain much. She had gone for the bag, just fifteen minutes before the ship sailed. Then she had met Charley Jim, whom she had never seen before, and whom she did not know. She had gone with him into the bush and the forest, and had remained with him until now.

"Save me from him, Mother," she begged. They promised to do so, and said that everything would be arranged when the bishop's instructions came with the next ship. Meanwhile she could begin teaching in the school.

Next day she was quiet and busy with her books. There were books in Latin—in French—in Greek. Moba was a language-genius, and she had all her school prizes with her here. But the Prioress thought that Moba should remain most of the day alone for a time—that she might find peace of mind in this way and think about what she had to do.

Four days later Moba vanished again. A mission in northern Canada is by no means a prison, and it is easy to escape through the windows. When a lay sister awakened everybody for early Mass, Moba did not answer. She had flown again.

Over a year passed. It was winter. Snow lay over everything, and the weather was bitter cold.

One fine day Charley Jim appeared, ready to trade. He brought his sled with him, and hitched to it were three dogs and a woman. No one would have believed that this dirty squaw had a Master of Arts degree from the Catholic College in faraway Quebec. But it was true. The woman was Moba.

Charley Jim walked by the sled on his snowshoes, carry-

ing in his right hand his fearsome Indian whip—its lash
a leather holster filled with shot. When such a whip is
used with force on the human body, the person feels the
effects for days. When he wanted to turn right, Charley
Jim didn't say a word, but struck out with his whip at the
woman and the dogs. The dogs howled, but the woman
only moaned. On her back she bore a bundle, and from
it one heard the whimper of a child.

The sled was heavily loaded, and it required a lot of
effort to pull it. Moba's skirt, which hung so far down
that the hem dragged in the snow, was poor and torn.
But Charley Jim did not stop until they reached the post,
and he went in to talk with the trader. The groups arriving today were no different from those one sees in such
places daily. The other squaws gathered around the
woman, questioning her and receiving answers from her.

They sat in their little tent. The fire burned before it,
and the tent was fairly warm when the Prioress and one
of the sisters entered. Moba looked up at them, but there
was no recognition in her look—only the same half-
unwilling greeting common to all squaws.

The Prioress spoke to her in French, and Moba answered in the same tongue.

"No," she said. "I don't want to come back. Charley
Jim wouldn't let me."

"But you are often hungry!"

"Well, I get enough food to keep me alive," she said.

"But those marks on your face—and look here—on your
shoulders." The Prioress pushed Moba's garment aside
and saw a thin, dirty shoulder, bearing red streaks from
whip lashes.

"He beats you. He is cruel to you."

"Oh, I don't know," said Moba. "One is treated according to one's merits."

"Moba, dear little Moba. What has happened—what have we done, that you ran away from us?"

"Stay in your house and leave me in my tent," said Moba as she rose and went out. The other two sat back, looked at each other, shook their heads, and went home.

The police sergeant was asked to register Moba and Charley Jim as a married couple. This was done, but there were no festivities in connection with it, since Charley Jim was in an ugly humor. He had had women before, and had deserted them when it pleased him, but he had never before been registered as a married man.

"You'd force me to it, would you?" he said to Moba. "Thought you'd get me into harness, did you?" And as they came out of the house, he kicked her until she fell over in the snow.

She picked up her mittens that she'd dropped, and didn't answer, but hurried off home.

Two years passed before anybody saw Moba again. Then Charley Jim arrived with a huge load of furs. He traded and bought many things—he even gave Moba a fine shawl and some trinkets. But now all his energy was gone. One often heard shouts of anger from his tent. That was when he was whipping Moba in his fits of rage. Maybe she'd asked for food for herself and her child. But no one ever heard her complain when he struck her.

One day she rapped on the door of the mission. She seemed like a stranger—just another Indian squaw who asked for food, and whose tongue ran like wildfire as she begged for everything she saw.

"Moba," said the Prioress, recognizing her. "It is Charley Jim who has forced you to come up here. I know you would never have come of your own free will."

"Isn't that his right?" asked Moba. "Isn't he my husband, my master, who decides what my life shall be?"

They gave her food. She came again.

Then the sisters told her she might come and bring her child, and eat all she wanted, but they would not permit her to carry food home with her.

"Good-by," said Moba. "Food is desired in my house." And she turned to go.

Another time when she stood aimlessly with the other squaws, the Prioress asked her to come and translate a difficult letter, written in Latin. She went willingly enough, for her husband had bade her go. He might as well profit by her learning.

A new look came over Moba's face. She was obedient and mild while she was at the mission house. This dirty squaw could be so tender and gentle. With her beautiful voice she read the difficult Latin letter, with its many Greek phrases, translating it into sonorous French.

Once she rose to get a dictionary from the shelf. There was a familiarity in all her motions—a routine in the way she opened the book. But when the letter was finished, she was again Charley Jim's wife.

"Pay me," she said.

They paid her generously, and let her go.

Letter after letter had come to her from the bishop. She merely laughed and read none of them. Now he came himself with the summer ship, and the aged man who so well understood her strange character asked to speak to her. But his messenger was sent back.

Moba didn't want to see any bishop. Partly out of sheer defiance, and partly too because her face was bloody and swollen. Her husband had maltreated her worse than usual.

But suddenly there was a big sensation in the village. It had been discovered that a trapper who used strychnine, and whom they had not been able to catch red-handed, had used Charley Jim as his go-between. Severe punishment for the white man, but even worse for Charley Jim. A seaman had delivered the poison to him, and besides, had brought whiskey to the village, and Charley had sent it to its destination. Now people knew how it was he could live for long periods of time without going on the hunt.

He was locked up and brought to trial, and all the Indians were called in as witnesses. This was to be a warning for the whole district.

But Charley Jim would not confess. "It's a lie. What they found in my tent was put there by my enemies."

"But the white man on the ship told us your name."

"He lied, and someone else used my name," insisted Charley Jim.

But the sergeant was not to be fooled.

"The strychnine was delivered—and it has been found —and you took the whiskey in your canoe farther down the river. How else could it be brought to the depot where our informant saw you? You will be sentenced without your confession. You can evade punishment only by proving that someone else is the guilty person. Otherwise you will be sent to prison for years."

There is nothing an Indian dreads more than confinement. To be deprived of freedom is his great fear, and Charley Jim looked around the crowd of Indians there as witnesses. He spied out one face and stared at it fixedly. Then he nodded his head and blinked his eyes twice. There was a stir among the Indians as a woman pushed her way forward.

"Do not punish the one who has done nothing. *I* smuggled in the strychnine. *I* was the go-between in the whiskey deal. When I was south I learned the white man's language—that's why I could do these things."

It was Moba who spoke. Everyone knew that she was lying. But Moba had confessed. An Indian squaw obeys her man's commanding look, even if she has passed the highest examinations and has a Master of Arts degree from the big college in Quebec.

3.

White Men's Ways

One day I was talking with an old Yukon Indian:

When people are young, you can't expect too much of them. You must grow old before you can realize that. I wish white people could learn that. But their brains are not so good as our brains. That I know.

I got my lesson a long, long time ago, when I was a boy. And if you have five dollars, I have a good story you can learn something from.

The story starts even before I was born. It was before the Americans came up to here to wash gold. There was a great priest here in the Yukon. He was a Catholic. He will never be forgotten. All the Indians loved him so. He understood how to make peace between people. Very few people were killed in his time.

But even this holy man had his faults. He could grow so terribly hot-headed in no time. When he was angry he never knew what he said or did. His name was Father Sougut, and when he got mad, he had to break something to pieces before he could calm himself down. Afterward people always told him that he was running the risk of killing somebody himself. And if he did so, they said, his Great Spirit would turn against him and push him down into a terrible fire and awful heat.

Now the Indians are very smart fellows. They always like to know how far they can go with a man. That's why they often tried Father Sougut, not to hurt him, you understand, but just to find out. Indians like to find things out. That's why they are so wise. Still they respected Father Sougut. (When he died they all cried.) But to get back to the story here is what happened:

Down south they had heard about Father Sougut, how wonderful a man he was. So after he had been up in the Yukon for ten years, he was made chief of a church down in Seattle. He was then called Bishop—that was the name they gave him—and he became a mighty man, who let somebody else do the floorsweeping and cooking. After he had been down there for some time, however, he was longing for his old friends up at the Yukon, so he went up to Alaska again to see the Indians. Once again they were all glad to have him around; everyone was happy even though they were sorry he was only a white man.

But Father Sougut, or rather Bishop, still hadn't learned to check his temper. Once in a while he got mad— there was always somebody who liked to try how far they could go with him. But he was always more kind afterward. Maybe that was why they often kidded him. One time he kicked a hole in the canoe the Indians were paddling. Another day he smashed his gun against the rock till the butt went to pieces. But he never attacked anybody, because that was a part of his priesthood, that he should never kill nor even jump at anybody. He only had to have something broken when his anger got worked up. People always got a kick out of this, yet they were quite scared when the bishop had his turns.

Bishop Sougut used to travel with a white man whose name was Frank. I don't know much about him except that he was a white man, and consequently did not understand much of people's minds.

Anyway one day he shot the Bishop. Perhaps the old man had been mad and Frank got afraid for his life. Nobody knows for sure. Well, the people came right after the killing took place. They were Indians from Kuyukuk, for the bishop was shot right where Kuyukuk runs out into the old Yukon.

They saw him lying there dead and miserable, so they took him up and buried him. He was so well liked that all of them felt sorry. They were so sad they put up a great potlasch in his honor, ate very much delicious food, and danced dances of mourning to him. One of the men, who was a poet, made a song about his good doings. That song was remembered and repeated several times since then.

Frank took part in the potlasch, and when he thought enough mourning had taken place for his dead partner, he said good-by and left. He gave some of the bishop's belongings to those who had buried him, still he said they could keep the stuff only on condition that they should never mention the killing to anybody. Most likely Frank was such a modest man that he did not like to be shown too much honor, because he had killed a great chief. He never liked to brag, he said.

But some of the things he had given the Indians were of no use to them. So they brought them to the trader in Nulato, and they also showed him some of those books that Father Sougut used to get his wisdom from. When the trader asked how they got them, some of them said that he was dead.

Nobody thought much about Frank any more, but after some time he was taken prisoner by the police down south in Sitka. Several people had asked him about Father Sougut, and he said that he had last seen him at Kuyukuk. Later on, he told somebody that the priest had fallen overboard from the canoe and was drowned. But the songs that were made in honor of the bishop were heard all over in the country by this time, the police understood them, and they learned from them that the bishop was shot. Then Frank was forced to confess. But he said that he had shot him because he was afraid he was going to be killed himself.

That was only the beginning; but after it great events took place. In the middle of the summer two policemen came the long way up to Nulato; they called all the Indians of the Kuyukuk tribe in, and asked them what they had seen. Then they dug down after the buried man and took a look at him.

Two of the Indians had seen Father Sougut right after he was killed. So the police asked them about many, many details. The chief of the police was a kind man; he was very polite. He wanted them to say that they had seen him alive. But he failed to say how much he would pay them for saying so, so the two men agreed just to tell the truth.

Everybody who was asked questions got something. The whole tribe got gifts. And the man who had made the song was asked to sing it again and again. He was given three packages with powder and a hundred bullets for his rifle. That, I think, is the first time a man has been paid just for words.

When the chief of the police had questioned everyone, he said he wanted the two men who had seen Father Sougut right after he died. They were going to follow him down to St. Michael, a place situated where the Yukon runs out to the salt sea.

When they came there they saw Frank. Frank had been brought there too. The death of Father Sougut was such an important event that every word was to be repeated in the white men's own land. So my two tribe fellows were taken on board a huge vessel and went to Seattle. There all the words were said again but still it was not enough. They were all taken aboard a new vessel even bigger than the first one, and everyone sailed farther south, down to Frisco. It was so warm and cozy they entirely forgot the forests and the people they came from.

Food came to them in big boxes. If they felt like eating they just rang a bell, then women brought them food. They saw a lot of houses on wheels that could be moved from place to place. People just entered and went out again when they arrived at certain places, where they had something to do. My two countrymen did not do a thing. Once in a while they were taken to a mighty big house—that was Frank's home. When he entered the room, he was always followed by men in fancy clothes, as if they were going dancing. And he sat in a special chair, where nobody else was allowed to sit. It was a special seat for those who killed bishops, I presume.

The two Indians had to repeat what they already had said several times. It was funny that the white men could not remember, even if they had written it all down in thick books. Finally the Indian men got the idea to tell something else, but this was not well liked. And as they did not want to be looked at as people who could not remember, they decided to say the same thing once more, and it showed that they were higher estimated because of that.

They had in mind to say that they too had taken part in the shooting of Father Sougut to obtain some of the same advantages that Frank alone now had; if they only had known more about white men at once, of course they would have said so. Now they had to stick to their first statement. After many days it was finally decided that Frank should remain in the big house for ten years. He was to be given food and warm clothes. During the winters he would have heat in his room, and he was not exposed to danger of any kind.

One day those two men returned home with big honors and lots of prizes. They were given two dollars for each day they had been away from home, and they were also paid for those words they had said about Frank's killing of Father Sougut. Besides that they were dressed in new garments, and each of them had a bag with extra clothes. They also were allowed to keep the blankets they had been using on board in the big ships. They had so many dollars to spend at the trading boats that the poor tribe turned around and became rich. And their settlement was by far the best one along the Great Yukon for many years.

And they had so much to tell that nobody in the houses felt the winter. The winter was too short that year! Everything was so interesting that people came visiting from far away. It was therefore no wonder that many envied those two men, and wished they could get such a journey and have food without any work and never feel the guts full of pain because they were empty.

My father was one of those who got a desire for traveling, and he thought it over for a long time, how he could manage it. And when the spring came and the snow melted away, he had an idea. White men had at that time started running around in the country, washing the earth out for gold. They used it to buy provisions. An Indian would always feel ashamed of working with the ground that never shows any resistance; it just lies there and calls for toil. But white men have committed lots of thefts and murders because of gold. If only they had gold, they could get everything else they wanted! The Indians know much about this; they have time and again been lying back of the bushes and shelters, and listening to what white men said to each other in this matter.

Then this summer some white men came down from Kuyukuk and they had plenty of nuggets and dust with them. They had nothing else. In fact, they were very poor except for gold.

The Indians amused themselves over these white men who very much lowered their race by doing such things as men ought not to do. They dig down in the ground and even if they get gold they never seem very happy about it. Often they were seen fighting, and if they had emptied a place for gold they never felt happy about it. When they went away no feeling of thankfulness was in them; they were dissatisfied all the time.

But now these men, who came down the Kuyukuk River, went to Charley River, and many others went up there. Also quite a few Indians wanted to see what took place there, and one of these was my father.

Two of the prospectors reached the river before the rest of them. One of them was called Tom, the other one, Jack. They each went in the direction where they thought it best for finding gold, and the next day they were to meet again and tell what they had seen. But Tom came first, and when Jack showed up at their meeting place, he found his fellow killed and robbed on the spot.

It happened that, as he stood and looked at Tom, he heard the rest of the men coming. They were hurrying to be the first ones after the gold, so he ran down to call for help. They all came up and saw the dead man, and at first they all thought it was Jack who had done it. But he told them he had nothing to do with the shooting, so they agreed to look around for the murderer. They saw soon that an Indian camp was close by, and they went there. But before they reached the camp, my father, who spoke some English, crossed their way. They asked him if he knew who shot the white man, and he answered:

Yes, I did it! I want to give myself up right here. I shot him because I want to go out traveling, and have my food brought to me, and live in a big house with many people, and be served upon by men in beautiful clothings.

They took him along to the camp; there they got hold of the older ones, who said that my father told them the truth. He had a long time ago announced that he was going to shoot the first white man he met, so he could get great experiences and return with much goods. He wanted to get a new wife, new guns, and warm clothes.

The golddiggers were awful angry. They did not think of the fact that my father did not hate Tom at all. My father had only decided to shoot the very first white man he saw—it might have been any of them. My father thought that this was his only possibility to go down to San Francisco—a place he wanted most badly to see.

Now the golddiggers got the idea of showing that it was forbidden to shoot white men, in spite of the fact that they rather often did the same thing themselves. And they agreed it was not enough to make the voyage down to San Francisco. If they had let my father alone, he, of course, could have found out himself that he had made a mistake, and then without doubt he would never have done any killing of anybody in the future, as he had no gain out of it.

They were—as I said—very excited. Still, my father had not done anything in anger. They were terribly mad at him. They took my father to the nearest tree with big branches. His hands were tied at his back. I can remember. I saw that.

Then they called all the Indians together and said many, many words to them: that it was forbidden to shoot white men. The one who did most of the talking spoke very loud to my father.

But he wasted his many words entirely, because right after he was through speaking they hanged my father, without giving him permission to show that he understood their ideas and intended to do what they told him.

After they had hoisted him up, they started shooting at him one after the other, and I remember, that in spite of the fact that he was already dead, he kept on bending his legs up every time they hit him.

I don't remember more from that day because I cried very much. I mourned over my father's death; he always used to be so kind to me. And my grandmother also cried intensely. I could not understand why my father did not crawl down from the tree and go away with us.

Two of the golddiggers patted me on my head and wanted to give me some provisions, but I was so foolish that I threw away what they gave me. My anger still could not bring my father back, but I felt hatred against the white people. I then went to some other places with my tribe, and we did not take my father down from the tree, because the white men told us that we were not allowed.

Later on we heard that nobody got any gold at the place; those who had been there at first had taken it all.

When the tribe returned to the same spot some years after, my father was not there any more. I don't know if some ghosts had taken him away because no ceremonies were kept to get them away, or if somebody had buried him. I was just a small boy at that time.

We were starving terribly that winter because the white men had scared all the moose away during the summer. After a while we were taught to go to other places, because the white men deprived us of our animals, so we had to learn new ways to make a living, and earn something by dealing with them. But it was easy to get money out of them, because we Indians are so much wiser than they are. They are like newborn babies, in this country where we have not only our own, but also the forefathers' experiences to take knowledge from.

From now on we all knew that it was not allowed to kill any people, but my father never had a chance to take advantage of what they told him. If somebody wants to murder his enemy he has to take care of not doing it in the open. He will be punished for being found out.

Even if I was so little I wondered why they never gave my father time to show that he understood what they told him.

But now I have seen, time and again, that white people are so stupid. They never can learn the wisdom of the Indians. They just think they are on the safe side because they are so many. Every year some of them go home to where they came from, but always somebody else will replace them. A few of those who stay here all their time learn to understand Indians, at least to some extent. But they never have so much to say as the newcomers, who talk out loud, and have lots of money in the pockets.

The Indians just keep quiet, and never let the white people see that inside they just smile, or that between themselves they often make hard jokes about the white ones. We only do that when we are at home, and sit around the fire, and talk about things. Then the young ones listen in, and that is why they become more and more wise. It is wonderful for the young to learn everything in this way.

The older a fellow grows, the more experiences he has. My father died very young, so he did not manage to collect much wisdom. But I am old, and I know so much. I learned it all from the white foreigners, but most of all from their foolishness.

4.

The Glass Eye

IT WAS A LONG TIME since men had penetrated this deep
into the Canadian forest, long enough for the animals to
have forgotten the trappers and the gold prospectors who
once roamed here without luck. Their gloomy reports
discouraged others from following in their wake, and the
quiet returned and thereafter remained unbroken. The
elk soon forgot the hunters, and the beavers gnawed con-
tentedly along the river banks, building their huts undisturbed.

Dr. Hebabian's small expedition traveled up river by
canoe. He and his two colleagues, Dr. Copp and Dr.
Smith, were geologists embarked on a government mission. Animals, fur, even gold, were of no interest to them
—only rock specimens. As strangers to the territory, and
unfamiliar with the ways of the wilderness, they hired six
of the best natives as guides and porters. They knew all
the hazards of such a journey, and they were absolutely
reliable through thick and thin—they said. Gentle Dr.
Hebabian, learned in books and laboratories but ignorant
of man's treachery, took them at their own estimation.

Slowly, without stamina but with great enthusiasm,
they pushed their way into the uncharted land, weary

from the difficult journey and the unfamiliar conditions. At first mosquitoes posed the biggest problem. They covered the land like smoke from an immense fire. They bit and they stung, and it was not possible to draw a simple breath without mosquitoes clogging the nose and mouth. No square inch of skin could be exposed, for these murderous beasts would immediately begin their attack on the vulnerable area. It was really something to hear the mild-mannered Dr. Hebabian succumb to cursing and swearing, but under the circumstances an angel from heaven would be hard put to smile graciously.

The Indians, however, were hardly aware of these troublesome insects, except when the fretting antics of the scientists attracted their attention. Having lived for so long in the forests, the Indian has developed an immunity to mosquitoes; and besides, when white blood is available, they almost never feed off the natives.

Netting was more a hindrance than a help. It was suffocatingly hot and made walking almost impossible. As a last resort the poor men were driven to smear themselves with an odious solution that, according to the florid label on the bottle, promised to keep these bugs out of biting range. But again, the cure was at least as bad as the disease. Its noxious smell discouraged the insects, but epidemics of headaches, nausea, and eczema attacked and demoralized the scientific party. Only Dr. Hebabian's faith in the label remained unshaken, and he attributed the ill effects of the remedy to a mistaken dosage or faulty application. He continued to smear himself regularly, and he concentrated all the more on his science to forget the pain of his burning flesh. "There is always a certain amount of discomfort when one travels," he reminded his tormented companions.

Additional problems were created by the numerous cascades that occurred along the river. It was impossible to paddle a loaded canoe against the current as it came foaming down over rocks and boulders. At such times the entire cargo had to be unloaded and carried along the bank until quieter water was reached. Anticipating this, they had packed the boxes in eighty-pound loads, which a man could carry strapped to his back. Actually it was the responsibility of the helpers to lug everything, but the scientists feared for their delicate instruments and their valuable notebooks. As a result, Hebabian, Copp, and Smith ended up carrying much of the cargo themselves.

For white men unaccustomed to the uneven terrain it was a slow process. In the time that it took them to make four round trips, the six porters had gone back and forth five times; and the Indians still had ample opportunity to loll by the riverside while the sweat evaporated from their foreheads and their hands cooled in the refreshing water. Finally their employers would arrive, straining under their heavy burdens.

These intervals were the most difficult for Dr. Copp, who had only one eye. For the first few days of the journey he seemed to the porters like everyone else, but late one night they were all awakened by a thunderstorm, and there—to the natives' horror—was Copp sitting up in his cot, with one of his eyesockets gaping emptily at them. All these men were accustomed to strange sights, but this was totally unprecedented. Tim, the half-breed, who was the largest and the strongest of the porters—as well as the laziest—let out a roar and bolted from the tent into the rain and lightning. Anything to get as far away as possible from that weird medicine man who had two eyes by day, and only one at night.

Although he was half white, Tim had been reared among Indians and had quickly forgotten the little that he learned during his short enrollment at the Catholic mission. He lived from hand to mouth, an existence that discourages deep thoughts about life. It was not one-eyed men that he feared, either—God knows they were common enough in this country—just so the missing eye was missing at all hours, day or night, every day.

After running for a while and getting soaking wet, Tim remembered his fondness for Dr. Copp who, of the three whites, was the most friendly. It was Copp who livened up the trip, constantly laughing, and singing for hours on end. Also, since none of his friends had followed him, Tim stopped, pondered the situation, weighed the dry tent against the rain and the darkness, and decided to risk going back. By the time he returned, a deep moat had been dug around the tent, which was still warm and comfortable. Tim had to endure considerable teasing from his more courageous companions until Ben, another half-breed, explained that there was nothing to fear. The doctor's missing eye wasn't missing at all. It was kept in a box alongside the doctor's cot, and obviously it was meant to be put in and taken out. This was no more peculiar than the other strange ideas and odd customs that distinguished the behavior of white men.

Yes, they all agreed, this whole trip was certainly crazy. For example, in the middle of a perfect traveling day the scientists would halt everything, start running around chopping small pieces from rocks, almost worshipfully examine the fragments, all the while chattering about them in some incomprehensible tongue. At last they would drop these bits and pieces into tiny pouches and rush to continue their journey up the river. One could understand white fur trappers, or those who searched for gold—things that were worth money. But this rock expedition was too silly.

Right from the start the Indians were suspicious of this trip. Ben had made certain in advance that they would be properly paid. The government's Indian agent who looked after their affairs was in many respects a scoundrel, forbidding life's simplest pleasures to the Indian; a man who had no appreciation for liquor even. But about money he was scrupulously honest, and when he gave his word on something, God himself would see that he kept it. Neither Ben nor Tim nor any of the others knew how this pact with God had been arranged, but it was a fact verified by all the elders of the tribe. There was no arguing against that.

So one day the arrangements were made, and on the next they were pushing slowly forward. Since the porters were paid on a daily basis, they were in no hurry; and since Dr. Hebabian was easy enough to convince, they managed to create all sorts of obstacles and difficulties and delays. Dr. Copp, on the other hand, despite his cheery disposition, was more suspicious. But on the whole, everything considered, the Indians were quite pleased with their employers, and most especially with themselves.

At long last they reached the spot that Dr. Hebabian

had chosen for a permanent camp site. From this base they would make various excursions during the next six weeks; and then, if all went well, they could start back for home. The camp was knocked together and a work schedule arranged. Every morning the geologists went out to beat the rocks with their hammers and gathered the chips which they carefully placed in the pouches together with little name slips—like people being buried in coffins. These were then packed in boxes for the journey home. How the carriers hated to see this baggage, day by day, growing heavier and heavier. Already their backs ached from the mere thought of carrying such a weight around the cascades. Stones are heavy no matter by what name they are called.

The carriers took turns accompanying the scientists, carrying their rucksacks and assisting them until evening. One native for each researcher. They did not enjoy this part of their work. True, most of the day's labor consisted in resting and waiting for twilight to come when the silly fellows would call a halt to their banging and digging. But it was very dull because they were not allowed to hunt on these excursions. To make matters worse, the white men never cared for the places that were readily accessible, but insisted on climbing the steepest ledges to expose themselves senselessly to the strong wind, even though there was probably a perfectly lovely lee nearby.

Only the three natives who remained in camp were permitted to hunt and fish. It was their task to replenish the provisions and see that fresh meat was available. Hunting and fishing was definitely more fun than hiking with a bag full of stones on one's back, and on the "hunting days" the Indians managed to recuperate from the exertions of the "rock days." As soon as the geologists left the camp, the three carriers whose turn it was to find game started their duties by going back to sleep. When they had snoozed sufficiently, they built a fire and cooked for themselves a substantial meal from the best of the available food supplies, taking great care to cover their tracks so that the losses would not be obvious. Dr. Copp supervised the provisions, and occasionally he was observed counting the biscuits. Since they were too dry for Indian tastes, there were never any biscuits missing. Tea and sugar were harder to gauge, and the good doctor felt that they were dwindling too fast. But they had taken plenty of provisions and he was not one to worry about such matters. Why make a fuss about a missing jar of marmalade or a can of milk? It seemed unworthy of him, Copp thought, to hold the Indians to a rigid accounting. Besides, his two colleagues took whatever supplies they liked in their rucksacks each morning, and he wasn't going to begin checking on them. And if worse came to worst there was always plenty of fresh fish available and lots of game, he hoped.

Those who remained behind did manage to keep the supply of food coming in. They would go off some safe distance from the camp, not too far, and the river supplied them with salmon; and when an unsuspecting animal ambled by, of course, they shot it. Ducks and geese, likewise, were plentiful and delicious. When they had enough of shooting and fishing, they slept, making certain that they returned to camp quite a bit after the geologists had settled down for the evening. This was to show that they spared no effort in their search for food, and to impress their employers with the variety and the quality of their kill.

Except for the mosquitoes which remained a constant irritation, Dr. Hebabian was entirely satisfied with the course of the expedition: with his colleagues, his helpers, and his own scientific accomplishments. He felt better and better as the weeks progressed; and much to the regret of his Indian attendants, he became more and more ambitious in his search for rock specimens, and his rucksacks became heavier and heavier. Each Indian prayed that he would not be picked on a rock day to accompany Hebabian who required twice as much lugging as the others did.

But even with the mosquitoes, life in the wilderness was wonderfully invigorating for the white men. They worked harder than they ever had before, and there was no time to fuss over anything so unimportant as their appearance. They let their beards grow wild, and this helped them against the insects; Dr. Copp even walked about with his eye socket bare. Under these rough conditions it was possible to work with a rare concentration.

One day, however, during the second or the third week at camp, something happened that threatened to unbalance everything. Ben and Tim and a third crony were enjoying a hunting day. As usual after their nap, they began to forage through the supply tent for anything that could be eaten or smoked without detection. It was Tim who uncovered the bottle in the wooden box, and attracted by the colorful label, he naturally had to try it. He poured some of the mosquito poison into his cupped hand and rubbed it into his neck and forehead and wrists, as he had seen the white men do. Ben followed his example. Soon the strange, pungent vapor enveloped them both, giving them a blissful sensation. Tim determined to probe further into the pleasures of this happy discovery. This time he opened the bottle and swallowed deeply several times. It made his throat smart, but amazing to say, the liquid really hit the spot. Almost immediately he was roaring drunk. His head hammered and his stomach threatened to explode. Stars filled his eyes, and the thunder of canon boomed in his temples. Never had he felt like this.

Tim did no hunting that day, and for that matter, neither did the other two who, having witnessed the miracle, also tasted the wondrous cider. When Dr. Copp returned that evening there they were in the tent, all three of them, dead drunk.

Later, when they revived sufficiently to answer the charges of their employers who formed an accusing group around them, the three Indians all claimed—as if they had rehearsed it beforehand—that it was a poisoned fish that made them so ill. By this time, Dr. Copp had found the empty bottle of mosquito repellent.

"You have been prying into my things and drinking from this bottle," he said. "From now on you will be under constant supervision, and there will be no more hunting days. From now on you will all go with us."

The culprits persisted in their story. At all costs they must avoid the terrible prospect of the stone-crammed rucksack every day. They denied and denied until the doctor turned on them and laughed in their faces.

"Enough of this. Do you see my glass eye lying here in the box? It *saw* you take the bottle out and drink from it. There is no use to deny it. I saw you myself through this eye. It *sees* everything, and from now on, it will lie on top of the box all the time."

Looking at them sharply with his good eye, he held the brightly shining piece of glass high over their heads. Under the weight of such a witness their alibi fell apart. They followed their confession with regrets and assurances and promises that this would never happen again.

Copp seemed to soften. Peace must be maintained in the camp. Man is weak. Temptations can overwhelm the sturdiest and most honorable natures. No use to cry over spilled mosquito repellent. What was past, was past. But he would not tolerate such conduct in the future. Solemnly he told them this.

"Oh, no! Never," the poor Indians stammered. "Never again. Never again."

But to make sure, the doctor would leave his eye out of the box from now on. In this way he could see everything and everyone who entered the supply tent. Everything was out in the open. There was no way to avoid the eye.

The weeks that followed were gloomy ones. No more sleep for the hunters; no extra rations. Grief oppressed them. On the other hand, the white men became even more cheerful than before. Now the stocks seemed quite ample. Sugar went further, and the coffee and tea were holding up fine. Copp's power over the natives was unlimited, and again and again he proved it to his colleagues, leaving the most tempting items lying about, and they were always still there when the scientists returned.

Tim was in a fury, but Ben pondered a solution to the problem. A situation in which the white man has the upper hand was intolerable. No Indian, particularly one with white blood in his veins, likes to admit defeat. That would be an acknowledgment of inferiority to the whites. Over and over, from every angle, Ben and Tim discussed and analyzed the dilemma. But there was the eye, scrutinizing their every move. Dr. Copp was triumphant.

But the victor cannot afford to sit back and rest on his laurels. Overconfidence breeds disaster.

One evening Dr. Copp returned to camp before the others, and he sensed immediately that something was wrong. Not only had Tim, Ben, and the third man disappeared, but it was obvious that they hadn't left empty-handed. The bottle of repellent was missing. The sugar bowl stared vacantly, like a giant glass eye, and only a few faint smears of jam remained in the jar that was almost full when Copp left that morning. The spell was broken, but this aroused the doctor's curiosity more than his anger. As a scientist, a man of learning, he was happy that even such simple people, raised on endless superstitions, were capable of reasoning clearly. Obviously they had figured it out among themselves that such an eye could never exist. For a while the doctor congratulated himself for having made a contribution toward the advancement of these poor souls.

But for a very brief while indeed. Afraid that the discovery of his fraud might have led them to damage the rather expensive eye, Copp hastened to the box on which he had left it. It was still there, except that now it was hidden beneath a large black felt hat that had been brought along on the trip for no good reason.

The doctor chuckled to himself somewhat ruefully. Education? Nonsense! The eye's magic was still strong, but in their desperate cunning they devised a scheme to get around it. They must have hung the hat at the end of a long branch, sneaked up from behind, and dropped the hat over the eye. Now the road was clear, and they were taking their revenge for the meager rations of the past weeks. It was Copp who learned the lesson.

Later, much, much later that same night, the three sinners returned. Shamelessly, arrogantly, they denied everything. Now they were absolutely confident that they were the masters of the situation. Nobody could possibly have seen them, not with that eye. Perhaps it was a bear, Ben said, who took the jam and ate the sugar. Yes, a bear, Tim agreed. Bears like sugar and jam, the third concurred. Didn't Dr. Copp see who entered the tent? Tim asked this, with a look of malicious innocence in his own clear eyes. The other two picked up the refrain, barely able to keep from laughing. Yes. Yes. Didn't the doctor see who it was through his glass eye?

From that day on, until they started back, all six Indians accompanied the geologists daily and lugged their rucksacks with grunts and groans. Twice a week they all had to go hunting to replenish the meat and fish supplies, and of course on these days the doctors accompanied them. This added to the delays, and the expedition was two weeks late getting home, which was all right as far as the porters were concerned since they were getting paid by the day anyway.

II.

WHITE MEN
OF THE
FROZEN
NORTH:
AMERICA

I.

The Best Food in
the Far North

MANY YEARS AGO, when I was traveling with Knud Rasmussen and two Eskimos, we lived for three full months on one thing, muskox beef. We ate it for breakfast, for lunch, and for dinner. We dreamed about it in our sleep. It haunted us on the trail. We seemed to be able to taste muskox beef in our mouths even before we chewed it.

One day, after I had finished a long trek away from the camp and was very hungry, Knud asked me a funny question. Of all the food in the whole world, he said, what did I think was the best thing to eat?

I thought my answer over for a while, but then decided that I could think of nothing more delicious or more agreeable to the taste than a nice piece of boiled muskox beef. And Knud quickly agreed with me! There was nothing in all the world, he said, as good as muskox beef. It was so good, he went on, that even if he should come across a good piece of caribou meat or a steak of a Black Angus, he would throw either to the dogs if he were sure he could get muskox meat in exchange.

This might seem to you like an effort to content ourselves with what we had, which was all we could get in the circumstances. If that was true, so much the better for us. But Knud and I felt the same way years later when we were dining together in Denmark, and were much disappointed to find that our delicacy was not on the bill of fare.

So much for what is really the best food in the world. But as everyone knows, the meal that tastes best is the one that comes to us when we are the most hungry. Peanut butter may seem like the fulfillment of an enchanted dream to a man in a foxhole. Snails, which most people won't even handle, are a great delicacy to the Japanese and French. The Bible tells us how John the Baptist lived on locusts when he was in the desert.

Understood in this sense, the best meal I ever had was a certain paste I prepared when I was on the verge of starvation. An Eskimo named Mala and I were traveling from Admiralty Bay to Milne Inlet. Halfway along the trail we ran out of food and had to subsist on grass and old rabbit dung. The latter, I can assure you, is even worse than it sounds; but a starving man doesn't trouble himself with matters of finesse. Then even this failed us, and we went for eleven days without the slightest taste of food. We were almost out of our minds with hunger and weakness. But we trekked onward and came down on the ice of a bay where we found the body of a seal.

With my snow knife I cut the brain out of the seal and placed it in blubber cut from just beneath the skin. I chopped all of this into a fine mash, mixed it into a paste, and put small portions of it on our tongues. As you know, a starving man must eat slowly. He doesn't have the strength to digest large portions of food. Our paste was just right for our condition—and our palates. Mala and I both agreed it was the best thing we ever tasted.

Many people may be curious as to the various dishes available in the Far North. I would like to tell you about some of the gourmet dishes of which I know.

The walrus's favorite food is clams and mussels. If he is caught just when he is feeding on them, his stomach will be filled with unshelled clams, partially digested mussels, and a combination of juices, green in color and almost as strong as whisky to the taste. (A walrus never has any clam shells in his stomach. He knows how to get rid of them.)

If you are tired of eating meat day in and day out, this combination will be a good and tasty balance for your diet. Hunters often bring it home for the women and children, much the way the American husband takes a box of candy home to the wife and kids. But be careful of this dish! The stomach juices of the walrus often prove to be too strong for those not familiar with them. So hold as much of this food as you can with both hands and wash it in sea water. The green juices will float off the top and sides, just enough remaining behind to give a tiny sour taste to the delicacy.

Speaking of walruses, let me say that boiled walrus meat is a very delicious meal in itself. It takes a long time to cook it and it is hard to chew; but it has a very tasty flavor that delights everybody. It can be served *aposok*, or only slightly boiled, as the Eskimos prefer it. Eaten this way the juicy meat smears the fingers with blood.

One part of the walrus, however, can be prepared very quickly. This is the diaphragm. You can always cut this out at once if you want a fast meal. Since it has no blubber or fat whatsoever on it, you have to have some blubber to go along with it for cooking.

The large blood vessel or aorta of the walrus is also delicious. It tastes almost like *mattak*, the skin of the narwhal. This is eaten raw and right after the walrus is taken; when it dries up it gets very tough and cannot be chewed.

You can also eat the flippers of the walrus. They taste exactly like pigs' feet. These have to be cooked, preferably boiled, and served warm. My first wife, Navarana, used to serve them to me and the children often. We were always excited to find them on our table.

The seal, the most common food in the arctic, is also one of the best. There is no part of the seal that cannot be eaten, though people usually acquire preferences for different parts. In the north where the men are always the ones to put meat in the pots, they get first choice, then their wives, and finally the children. I always chose the ribs with the blubber sticking to the meat. Knud Rasmussen liked various parts. When the pot was ready, he either cried "Tajarnak," meaning the upper arm, or else chose the jawbone with the tongue.

The intestines of the seal are also very good, and I know many northern people who yelled for this when the meal was cooked. They can even be eaten raw, except that the innermost layer is too tough for this and must be thrown away.

Young seal meat is a seasonal dish in the Far North. It can be had only in springtime, when the pup has taken nothing but its mother's milk. Then its meat is tender and white and its stomach full of yeasted milk or cheese.

The latter makes very fine soup, though not everyone likes the sour taste.

Another special seal delicacy is the liver. I never met anyone who didn't like it, raw or cooked, whether in combination with another dish or with the green stomach juices or eaten alone. Stiff, frozen seal liver tastes like chocolate and has to be eaten with a good deal of blubber to get it down. Boiled seal liver, which becomes light in color, has an entirely different but equally enjoyable taste. It is more like crabmeat than anything else, although its taste is still unique. Again, seal liver can be thrown into a meat cache to rot. In this case it becomes green and its taste is exceptionally delicious.

There are many types of birds in the arctic—all of them delicious and easy to prepare. The little auk, which is found by the billions in the districts around Thule, is eaten only in cooked form in the spring and summer. If it is not going to be used at once, however, it is usually made into *igunao*. To make this, the auk is strangled by applying pressure to the heart; this causes it to bleed inside, forming a big clot within the chest and stomach which turns out to be most tasty. Many like to stuff six or eight hundred such auks into a fresh sealskin, add a lot of blubber to it, and then put the whole bag under stones or dirt to rot. The auks then absorb the seal oil, and their white feathers turn rosy. Nothing is more delicious to eat.

Some of these dishes may sound strange to those who have never been to the Far North. But they're really excellent in themselves and the most desired foods of all in places where many Danish and American dishes would seem strange to the natives.

2.

Trading in the North

MANY YEARS AGO, I went to the place in Greenland which we called Etah. The Eskimos there had seen Americans before—one of them, fortunately, that great explorer who discovered the North Pole, Admiral Robert E. Peary. Great as was Peary's record of exploration, he was outstanding as an educator of people. Every year from 1892 until 1909, he went up there, educating the young Eskimos to be good hunters and good travelers and teaching them many things. Finally, with their help, in 1909 he reached the North Pole with dog sleds.

When I went there, all Eskimos were seal and walrus hunters. They went to sea alone in their kayaks, harpooned seals and walruses and whales, and brought them home. The returning hunter was a great man, but everyone was allowed to come and take his share. It was a sort of communistic life, with everyone who was there entitled to a piece of the meat—and no need to thank anyone for it, since this was a communal right.

Exploration in the arctic is sometimes difficult—and the most difficult part, as I learned, is to raise the money to pay for it. So the late Knud Rasmussen and I formed a partnership to establish a trading station at Etah. It was our purpose not only to earn some money for our future expeditions, but also to meet a need which existed there. After the Peary expedition had reached the North Pole, nobody had returned to this area. The Eskimos there had acquired guns from Peary, as well as knives, hatchets, matches, and supplies of that sort. Now they had no more ammunition and no way to repair these tools or replenish other supplies. In addition, Rasmussen and I felt we could teach these people to help themselves.

However, we found it quite a task to teach them how to trade, for the Eskimos had no knowledge of values. For example, an Eskimo with his family would travel a long distance to our trading post because he wanted a knife. Perhaps he would bring, say, ten blue-fox skins. We would try to tell him that a knife costs much less than ten blue foxes. He would reply: "I need this knife very badly— I have been the whole summer without a knife, and there were so many times I needed one that I wish to pay very much for it, because the more I pay, the more happy I feel about having a knife."

Or another time, an Eskimo family would arrive with two big bags of blue-fox skins. They would tie their dogs outside and put their meat and these bags of blue-fox skins up in the meat racks, out of reach of the dogs. Then they would come in and we would treat them as guests for several days. Meanwhile, they never mentioned that they had come to trade. After two or three days, I would casually ask the head of the family if he had some blue-fox skins. He would answer: "Me? Oh, I am a poor hunter. No, I have not brought anything that is worth anything at all." So, I must then say that I had heard he is a good hunter and I am sure he has brought some very fine skins. Again he would protest: "Oh, I have some poor skins, but they are worth nothing at all. Even if they had been good, my wife has spoiled them, because she does not know how to prepare them. She spoils everything, I would not want you to see them."

Then, I would say, "But I thought you had come here to trade." To this, he would answer, "No, I don't want to. The skins I have are so bad, I would be ashamed for you to see them." Finally, I would persuade him to bring in the skins and they would make a big pile on the floor. He and his wife would say, "Let us go outside. We are so ashamed for you to see these terrible skins we have brought." Now, it would be my turn to praise them as wonderful skins and to protest that we did not have any articles worthy of exchange. This would go on for several days, before an exchange was worked out.

That was before the first World War. I was up there again after the second World War, and it is quite different. An Eskimo comes in with some fox skins, lays them on the counter, and says: "I have some very fine blue-fox skins here and my wife, who is a very clever woman, has taken very good care of them, so you will have to pay a very good price for them." A price is agreed upon and the trader counts out the money in one-kroner notes, which makes a bigger pile. Then the Eskimo starts with his list of items he wishes to purchase. As the trader takes back the money, the pile gets smaller and smaller. Perhaps the Eskimo will say, "Give me back my money. I have changed my mind. I want to get something else." Because, you see, he now knows that he is a man who can command, and the white man who stands there has to obey when he changes his mind.

Other things have changed, too. In southern Greenland, the temperature is now higher. The ocean water is
getting warmer. The seals and the walrus have moved
further north. But when they left, the codfish moved in.
Every year, more than four thousand Portuguese fishermen come there to fish in the Davis Strait and along
the south shore of Greenland, together with more than
thirty-five hundred Frenchmen and an additional ten
thousand Danes, Norwegians, Englishmen, Spaniards,
Italians, and Americans. No longer does an Eskimo go
out alone in his kayak. Now he goes out in a motorboat
with others, and they work as a team. At one time I was
associated with a fishing company which bought from
these Eskimos. And when a boat brings in, say, ten or
twelve tons of fish, and the fish have been piled on the
dock and paid for, we must still get them cleaned. But
these Eskimos, who have made big money on a good
catch, do not wish to sit down and clean fish for wages.
Neither does it interest their wives and daughters to work
for a few kroner cleaning fish, when they have seen their
husbands or fathers come home with more than a hundred
kroner for a day's fishing. Or if you get them to work
at the fish, and you have a number of girls cutting out
fillets, happy and singing at their work, perhaps one of
them looks out and sees an iceberg. Then she may say,
"I want to go up on the mountain and look at the sea
and the iceberg." And away they all go to the mountain,
while your fish spoil!

Fortunately, I speak their language and I understand
these people. We must get them to understand that the
fish are no use to us unless we can get them cleaned. We
must praise them and tell them how surprised we are to

find how good they are, but if they would do a little more how much better they would be. No longer do we encourage them to be modest in their want of things to make life more pleasant. Because we want more production, we want more money in circulation. To get more production, the only way is to have more articles in the stores for the people to buy. So it is that now these Eskimos can buy nice houses, they can buy motorboats, furniture, all kinds of canned goods, a wide variety of cloth and clothing, or whatever they might wish for. Anything you could buy in Denmark can now be bought in southern Greenland. And as these people get more ambitious to own more things, they become more and more industrious. They are living witnesses to one of the great social miracles of our time—the transition of a whole people from the stone age to machine and space civilization within the life-span of one human being.

3.

Strube's Story

I DON'T KNOW WHY I was always left behind. I was a weakling in school, or at least they thought so. Maybe they were right. I never could make good anywhere. I was not stupid, but the teachers never let me prove my ability. I was shy, and stuttered when I was faced with exams, so I always had bad marks. At gymnastics I could never keep up with the rest of them. On the football field I told myself that I was just as good as any, but nevertheless everything went badly for me. I always had an explanation for myself, but it made me bitter and unsociable.

I knew that the rest of the boys didn't like me, but I always had the impression that they were to blame. Always unsuccessful!

For instance, I was a good marksman, but the very day we had the prize contests something went wrong for me. I never got any prizes, in spite of knowing I was better than those who won the awards and had their names in the paper.

I was doing the arithmetic homework for many of my classmates, but at the final examinations I happened to make some mistakes, so my marks were far inferior to those who did not know as much as I did.

Such was my entire childhood. At the proms the most popular girls never danced with me, and I could not understand why. If I tried to date any of them, they just laughed at me, and I was envious of the other boys, who could talk to the girls freely and without embarrassment. I saw time and again that I was a laughingstock, and what I did not see, I felt deeply. Then came the graduation. I had been very conscientious and hoped for a good grade. But again everything was against me. I was just asked the few questions I did not know anything about, and there I was, barely scraping through.

At home I was blamed and scorned, and every time I tried to prove myself I was scolded.

As soon as I went to college, my father died, and there was not money enough to see me through. With my record and the fact that I was very unpopular, it was impossible for me to obtain a scholarship. So I had to go home and be glad to get a job in the office at the factory. It looked like I would spend the rest of my life in that office.

I remember that when the rest of the boys came home for vacation from college they overlooked me entirely. Little by little they did not even recognize me any more. I was just an office clerk, poorly paid, and this would keep on until I was laid in the graveyard.

Then it happened that I fell in love. I knew all right how ridiculous it was, but what could I do? I dreamed about Johanne night and day.

Unfortunately my daydreaming made my work even poorer and worse than before, so I was warned again and again to try and improve.

When I finally collected enough courage to tell Johanne what I felt for her, she just smiled, rather kindly, and told me she was engaged to be married to Valdemar, the boy who always had been the worst to me. He tormented me. This was a blow I could not take. Before Johanne had told me this, I had taken her to the theater, and to dinners in the park, and so on. In fact I was deep in debt. Now this was to be paid off, and would take me years and years. What a future!

How I finally got hold of myself I don't know, but one day I sold everything I had, got what my sisters and brothers could spare, and went off to America. Over in the old country they always had the idea that you could go to America, make a million in a year, and then come back and really show them something.

I might have had the same idea. In any case I was so badly off that any change had to be for the better. So off I went.

In New York I found that it was not so easy as I had thought. Of course I knew I had to begin at the bottom, and this I did without hesitation. But it was not so easy to climb up, and as my hopes faded, my old insecurity popped up inside me. New York was not for me, but then I heard several people offer the same advice, "Young man, go west!" That was the recipe in those days, and I thought there might be something in it. So I worked hard, ate less, and finally I managed to save enough to buy a ticket to the west coast. I soon found out that the Pacific did not wash the gold up on the beach. The work was just as hard in San Francisco, and many people, especially the Chinese, could do manual labor cheaper than we whites could. And well-trained longshoremen were stronger than I was. Then I tried as a waiter. My co-workers stole from me. Always I had bad luck. There, as in New York and as at home, bad fortune followed me.

Then, one day, I happened to get a job with a contractor by the name of Strube. He was not any special kind of man, but he gave me some work, and in the beginning I was pushing a wheelbarrow, on a job he had, digging foundations.

One day we were down there and had to figure out some mathematical problem. I did it for Strube and that was how he found out that I had a better education than the rest of them.

He took me in, to the office. After a while he saw that I was honest, and little by little he made me his cashier and accountant, but still for a very small wage. But I could not afford to leave the job.

I could easily see, when I became more familiar with his business, that he could have done much better if he had more money to invest, but often he had to let several contracts go because he did not have the funds to pay the workmen, and banks were not wild to give loans to an unknown. One day we talked about this and he told me about Alaska. Up there, he said, there are big chances for a man who has some technical knowledge and can draw a design. By that time I knew a little about his jobs, because he drew the plans and I was the one who figured out the costs. I kept count of everything.

He still paid me very badly, yet I was all the time afraid of being fired. I was a coward there, in San Francisco, as I had been all my days. I was too cowardly to stand up for myself. I was too cowardly to walk out and try to find something better.

Strube had soon found that out. I, for my part, was

aware of it, and this made me even more angry with myself. I could see clearly that he took advantage of my uncertainty and depended on my weakness. I could see it, but I couldn't do anything.

One day he came and told me he had decided to give up his business in San Francisco. He and I were to go to Alaska.

He had just signed a contract for a good piece of work. He now sold this to a couple of young men. He got money for the fare, and he gave the order to be ready to travel in a couple of days.

He then added, as a matter of course, that we could go on under the same conditions as up until now. He added that he depended on me, and I was stupid enough to agree.

The moment I answered him I regretted it, but then Strube had gone out the door, and the next day I dared not take it up again. I was sent out to buy different things, and I had to take care of some business for him. So I did not see him before I went to Seattle, where I just reached the boat a few minutes before it was ready to sail.

The first thing I found out was that I was to travel on deck, while my employer had a first-class cabin for himself. I got angry about this, but on board everybody was occupied in taking leave and accommodating himself. I had no opportunity to tell him the first day out, and later on I thought it was too late. So I kept silent.

The journey was like such journeys are. I met a bunch of people who were all looking out for themselves. They pushed and struggled to make the best out of it. We slept in bunks for four on the between deck, and I got the worst of it—an outside place in an upper bunk. At meals everybody grabbed the best pieces, and soon they found out I was not somebody to consider a competitor at the table. As a result I had to be content with what was left over. As usual, I was the weakling, but I hoped that everything would improve when we reached Alaska. In fact, I have been an optimist all my days in spite of my bad luck. I always thought that good fortune lay in wait for me somewhere. But it never dawned on me to do anything to catch up with it. I never tried seriously.

As we reached Alaska and were about to embark, Strube emerged from his first-class cabin. I had not seen him at all during the voyage. He looked me up and started giving orders about the luggage. Most of the passengers were young men with adventure on their minds. All of them saw huge opportunities, and several proposed that I join them—they foresaw big money. But I was a hired man; I had my obligations to my employer. He treated me disdainfully, and I was well aware he knew I would never dare to run out on him. How I hated him for that!

So we went up to the interior of Alaska. At that time the possibilities for traveling were far more limited than now. No roads, and of course no automobiles, and even though some years after the great gold rush had taken place, many parts of Alaska were unexplored. Most people were just set on prospecting in new districts or intent on cleaning out the old ones in a more rational manner than the first gold hunters had done.

Strube and I traveled together with a few men who wanted to go to Alaska instead of following the usual trail into Canada where the Klondike was thought to be the only worthwhile place. We worked north from Valdez, and that was a hardship, the like I had never been up against before. But I had better treatment during the trip, as every attempt at authority faded out of itself. Here only partnership could save our lives, and we reached Fairbanks where we met several men who had been in Alaska from the first gold rush time. They all understood that the time was gone when it would pay to sit with a pan by the river and wash for gold. Now, larger machinery was needed. They also knew that it would pay to have an educated engineer along who knew machines and the theoretical part of the game. So Strube was soon hired by some big moneyed men, who knew places they regarded as so stocked with metal that it would justify the expenses a large industrial plant would cost.

I must admit that Strube knew his trade in every detail. He was a very practical man, but was a hard man, and he knew no mercy for anybody. His plans and drawings were good enough, but I had to do all the figuring. He was very bad at counting sums. When I had made everything out and explained it to him, I knew he added a considerable amount to the expenses because he always wanted to make more than the wages he had contracted for. But I never did get any kind of a slice for myself. Strube treated me exactly like a slave, and I hated him more and more. But I hated myself even more for submitting to it all and for not exposing his swindling, for not leaving him. He saw it, and he realized that the worse he treated me, the more miserable I grew. He knew that by whipping a creature, one creates dogs! I obeyed him but my hatred increased and grew so big that I knew I would be unable to stand it for much longer.

Strube and I were to stay alone at the place during

the winter, and wait for the machines and the crew that were to arrive by the first boats on the Yukon after the ice had gone. The moneymen had already had enough. They left us to go back and sit down in the States, and collect the profit out of our toiling on their lots and with their equipment.

To be alone with Strube was worse than anything else. He put me on all the tough work. I did the cooking and dishwashing. I chopped wood for our stove and hauled water from the river. Strube let me carry water up in pails for his hot baths. This was maybe the worst of it— to haul up all that water and see him let it purl down over himself. We were alone, the two of us, and two men alone in the wilderness can hate each other in a way nobody who hasn't experienced it can understand.

Strube had no idea what I was thinking about. He did not estimate me to be dangerous. He abused me and gave orders. Besides letting me write and count, he put me at shoveling snow and chopping wood, and all the work in the house and outside. Himself, he just drank and scorned me, or he ignored me entirely. I was too low for him.

It was in those days I decided to kill Strube. I sometimes wondered why I had not had that idea before. But I intended that this was to be revenge not only for Strube's behavior, but for all the humiliation I had been exposed to in my entire life. He was to die. I had been preparing for this a long, long time by pretending to be so weak and cowardly. I really looked forward to all the advantages I was to have in the future. But my plans were to be formed very carefully—in so fine and cunning a way that nobody could ever find out what had taken place.

I would fix it all so nobody would miss him; he was to disappear entirely.

But I did not kill him. This is the truth. I swear I did not kill him, in spite of my firm intention to do so. I had been out to shoot something for our kitchen. Strube had gone for a stroll, and he had seen tracks of moose near by. But he had no desire to be out for many hours when he could send me instead. Also he disliked the idea of skinning and carrying meat on his back. So he told me to hurry out on my snowshoes, but he said I had to be back within twelve hours, as the ice might break up any time.

With that the men would come up with their loads, and lots of preparations were to be made—of course by me. Strube never thought of lifting a hand himself.

But when I returned home, Strube was not there. I went right into our hut from the forest. The fire on the stove had burned down. Everything was untouched, and Strube was gone.

At first I was terrified; I thought he had found out, and now stood somewhere ready to shoot me down. It was entirely crazy to think so, but as I harbored just the same intention, it was logical.

He lay down at the river—dead. No sign of violence or shooting; he had just fallen. A heart attack or a stroke —how could I find out? Strube was dead, that was all I knew, and there I stood. It was like an unexpected wonderful gift dumped on me. I was relieved not to be a murderer. To tell the truth, I am now not absolutely sure that I would have committed it at all; maybe I would have backed out in the last moment. But here was my enemy dead—by himself. And all my careful plans could still be carried out. I had repeated, time and again, what to do and how, when I could not sleep nights, or when I was hauling water and fuel for him—when I saw him eating the choicest pieces of our food—yes, during every hour of the day.

I remember distinctly that it took just a second. A great change took place inside me. It was because I did not have to kill him. It was a burden taken away from me—from now on I would never be the weakling any more.

Finally, I had the upper hand. My deserved portion in the world had come to me! Not that I felt exactly happy; suddenly it was all natural to me that I, and nobody else, was the one to decide. The Boss—that was me now!

I was entirely calm when I buried him in the frozen soil. I knew all his plans by heart. I used to take care of everything. What was to be fixed, I fixed. In no time I grew very smart, so I was absolutely sure I had nothing to fear. And all this was because I had nothing to blame myself for. I had not killed Strube, and I now had my reward for all my misfortunes in life. It would be foolish, in other words, it would be immoral not to take advantage of it.

So when the boat arrived, I received the four men who went on shore with great regret. My assistant and good helper had died this very spring. Because of that, I had not been able to prepare so much as I had intended for their arrival. But they all seemed very contented with everything, and they told me that the hired men would be up on the next boat. I had no reason at all to doubt that they believed everything I said. Of course I had secured all Strube's papers and credentials. I showed them casually to the four men, who in their turn told me how wonderful it was to have a scientific, educated engineer up here in the wilderness. They treated me with the politeness I very soon felt I deserved.

And when the crew of workers arrived we started everything according to plan. We built houses, we blasted rocks, and on a certain day we got news that some experts would come and take a look at everything. The owners had formed a great stock company and were going to sell all their shares, so the inspectors were coming.

Real fine scientists came up, geologists whom I spoke to as equals, and they found the prospect very promising and went away again with the first boat to go down the Yukon. The next message we received was that a big company had taken over, and they offered me the job as chief engineer at the mine. But I refused. They felt very sorry but thanked me for my doings so far, and gave me a nice final accounting, and so my Alaska adventure came to an end.

I did not go down to Seattle with the boat. I went on shore in Victoria and from there I crossed over to Vancouver. I feared meeting people who had known Strube.

I now had money, more than I had ever possessed, and I got the idea that I better go home to the old country and show them all—especially Johanne.

But I didn't take the boat right away. I went down to the States and met some people in the big city where I was later to become known. My new friends were kind to me, and told me that they were stockholders in the mine I had opened, and they felt sort of obliged to me for my work. I answered that I had just done what I was paid for, but they protested and said that my reputation had been widespread and the shares were way up in price. I liked to be recognized. I didn't give a single thought about not really being the German engineer Strube; I was already so used to the name and the title that it was all mine. And, as everybody was kind to me, I stayed for some time, and soon found myself in the middle of a political campaign. I had no intention of horning in, but my friends were involved in local elections, and I liked being asked about the running of the town. So I took a hand in the city's politics, even though I was only there for a few months. But then I was put up for the job of doing all the public engineering work in the city. I felt flattered—no wonder—and I was elected.

One day I found myself sitting in a big office where I had a huge staff of clerks and secretaries. Out on the streets a whole army of people were sweeping and cleaning and drilling and digging—working for me. We had plenty to do. But little by little I found out that this was no worse than what I had had to do with before, and as they all showed great respect for my decisions, it was easier for me. It sort of flattered me, and I liked my job. Furthermore I found out many leaks where money could be saved for the taxpayers. We never, of course, kept this away from the public. So I grew popular, even though I closed my eyes to some large commissions paid to the different politicians from those who got contracts with the city. They all made money out of their jobs, but I refused. I made a point of it, and I had my precise motives. I wanted to be admired. I had a good enough salary to live comfortably. And I also was aware that nobody ever before had seen such a thing—refusing to take a share but rather make everything less expensive for the city.

I eventually got a reputation not only for being honest, but also for being able to get everything at reasonable prices. This made the city council regard me as a good man and they decided to materialize what had been discussed for many years: a bridge across the river. Lots of trade would cross it and they would all benefit.

One day I sat in my office, not realizing what was up. The mayor and some of his advisers came to me and told me that the bridge approval had been granted. Would I start figuring out and design a really magnificent bridge that could be a monument for the city and a pride to the inhabitants.

There I was! I could not confess that I was not able to do so. I could not tell them that I was not a bridge-builder, so I at once thought that I might better quit and take leave. This bridge would in any case expose me, because I did not possess the required skill and knowledge.

But I did not let any of the high officials know my feelings. I assured them that I was the happiest man in town. Now I would have to show myself capable of doing more than sweeping streets and repairing sewers. I was going to make them a bridge generations would be proud of. At the same time I told them that preparations would take time, and I might have to travel to see other bridges, since I would have to examine materials and so on. I promised them some designs as early as possible so the council might decide the appearance of the coming connection between the two banks of the river. Only then could I start figuring out about the cost of the amount of materials and what else was essential.

I decided at once to jump the place entirely. I had money enough to go home and live, and I had had the wonderful years of being regarded as a great man. Now it was over, but I did not regret it. Back in my mind had always been the feeling that this would come to an end sometime, and now this way certainly was an agreeable enough one.

But the next night, when I was sleepless because of the big decision I had to make, I got a bright idea, an unusual idea, as I lay there, and I could hardly wait until the next morning to go to the mayor and explain it to him.

"Here we have an occasion," I said, "to really put this town on the map! Let us put up a big prize and let some of America's best-known bridge-builders compete. I will then supervise what they turn in to make sure it is sound and reliable. Let the papers all over the country write about the competition. That will let many hear about what opportunities are combined with putting up new factories here. This will bring tourists, and the entire population will profit. Of course," I told the mayor, "I would like to do the job myself." But I was somewhat modest, too, and said that if somebody was fit to do a better job than myself, I would at once recognize him and approve. This was all meant for the benefit of the city and not for me.

The mayor remarked that he knew my noble personality and he certainly appreciated it, but he would have to confer with his council first and then let me know.

It was decided to address five of the best-known professors at technical colleges in the country and ask them to forward their ideas of a bridge. They all went along, and I had many conferences, during which I picked up many technical terms I did not know before. Some of them might have found out that I was not too bright an engineer after all, but as I was the one to make the decision they were all very polite and helpful and not too curious.

When the deliverers of material found out I refused any kind of reward for giving them contracts, they too respected my honesty. I was well aware that the city bosses would find out about this, but I took care to let people know I did not want anything for myself but my salary.

There was an immense festival when the bridge was finished after three years. The governor was present, and people from near and far came to our town. The bridge was wonderful, and I was the one to get the credit. Of course I told everybody I was just the supervisor, the real bridge-builder was the professor from the famous college who had now added a new star to his reputation. That went very well in his circles, but so far as the public went, I was regarded as the one who had given the bridge to the place that now was going to boom because of the expected trade with the other side the river.

Everybody was happy. The mayor and the council loved me for my supposed honesty. This had given them an opportunity to get more for themselves out of the expenses. They decided to reward me with a huge donation—said to be only a minor part of what I had saved for the city by keeping the expenses down. That, in fact, saved all of them from closer examination of how the money was really spent.

But I kept a careful watch. Such a task would not be finished without much ado in the press, and especially in technical magazines, and these are read all over in the world. I knew this, because I myself had studied designs of bridges from everywhere. So I never had any doubt that this would be seen in Germany, where engineer Strube from the *Mitweida Technicum* would now be written up. And sure enough I got several letters from friends and relatives—all of whom were surprised, and asked why he had never written them before.

I also had messages that some old colleagues of his were now in this country who would come to visit. Now I knew that my time was up.

I explained in my answers that I was tired from the huge work I just had completed. I was to take a trip to Florida for a month, but then I would be happy to see them here and show them my bridge and my home and what not.

I never let anybody know that I would not be back. I left everything but my bank account. That was already sent to different places in the old country. Not to any single bank over there; I was too smart for that. And then I left for my vacation.

That was the end of my story. On board the boat I took my old name up and I went at first to England and France. Then I finally made for the old home town.

Modestly I had left it, and modestly I returned. Of course it was a sensation that the funny little good-for-nothing boy had really come back. At first they did not know how to treat me. I had my fun by watching my old boss at the factory, who met me on the street and asked me if I had a desire to get my old job again. He told me that he just happened to have an opening for me. Politely I thanked him, and told him I would rather think it over.

The next week I bought all the stock in the factory, but let him know that he could keep his job as the manager, provided he could do it after I had changed the entire run of the plant and renewed the machinery and methods of trading.

Finally I had all the fun I had been starving for all my life. My sisters were taken care of nicely, both of them were married, and one of my in-laws worked as a traveling salesman for the factory I had just bought. He was the one who was married to my oldest sister. What a delight to humiliate her with my generosity and give him a raise.

But most of all I had pleasure in seeing Waldemar and Johanne. They were running a small business in town. He had still his old arrogant manner, and he tried at once to let me know where I belonged. That was before I had shown him very clearly that I was a man of means. Then he changed entirely.

They all did. Every one of them showed how humble they were to the one they had overlooked from his childhood.

4.

The Pangs of Jealousy

EXPLOSIONS AND CRASHES — every time the smoke cloud parted to let a larger spark fly upward it sounded as if someone had shot a bullet into the fire. Nothing could be done: the police barracks were afire, and they were soon surrounded by a sheet of flame.

People stood gasping for air—fresh, cool air to fill their lungs and ease the coughing spells.

Johnny put his arm about her and drew her close to him.

"Ah, Mabel, Mabel! I was beside myself with fear—you looked as if you were dead! Are you faint? Can you stand alone?"

He brought his face close to look at her. The young woman was pale, and of course she was frightened. She really *had* been afraid—and who wouldn't be?—to be thus torn from a deep sleep to find the roof overhead afire, and have to find clothes and dress in an instant! It seemed as if the courageous, unconquerable Mabel, who had traveled with her father until he had fallen on the ice-fields, was now but a helpless little woman. Johnny, in spite of his fear and disturbance, thought it made her even more lovable. He, who loved her for her spirit and courage, now found in her for the first time an appealing feminine weakness, a weakness which must seek the help of a man.

"Stay here, Mabel—I'll be right back," he said. She gave a little cry of fright, but he was gone, and she saw him rush into the burning house. The smoke hid him, but he soon reappeared, his arms full of books and papers. These, she knew, were the service records. His pale face was lit by the flames, as he stood before the door gasping for fresh air.

But Mabel was not the woman to allow herself to sink into helplessness for long. Now her senses were clear again, and she sprang forward, calling to her husband.

"Johnny!" she shouted. "Johnny, get out of the way. Let me get inside. I must get into my room. There's something in there that must not be lost."

"It's impossible, Mabel! No one can get in there now. A ceiling beam just fell. It just grazed my cheek. No, you mustn't dare go."

"I must, Johnny, I must! Do you hear? There's something there that must not be destroyed. If you knew what it meant to me, you wouldn't hold me back! Johnny, Johnny," she screamed at the top of her voice. And she looked at him with such prayer in her look—such a pleading for help, that he knew that it meant more than life itself to her—whatever it was she *must* and *would* save.

"No, Mabel, it's impossible, because the ceiling beams have fallen. But I'll try. What is it you want? Tell me, what is so important that you'll risk so much for it?"

"Oh, Johnny," she begged. "Oh, if you *can*, you *must* do it. Listen. In my little box by the window are two bundles of letters. I must have them. Get them for me if you love me!"

Startled, he raised his head. Letters! Yes, now he re-

membered how many times he had seen the two bundles
of letters tied together with a rose-colored ribbon. Twice
he had jokingly asked what sort of epistles these were.
But Mabel had soberly told him that they were confiden-
tial letters, written before she knew Johnny, and since
then Johnny had never asked about them.

"Is it the two bundles of letters?" he asked.

"Yes, yes," she whispered, trembling. "Listen, Johnny—
don't ask, but get them for me."

He saw her eyes and the pleading look about her mouth.
He needed no further incentive. What if he *did* have to
rush into a burning building again? Wasn't it worth the
risk to satisfy such a furious desire of Mabel's?

He was gone. The flames closed behind him. The
Indians who stood about howled with fright, and Frank
rushed over to Mabel and seized her arm.

"Why did you let the staff sergeant go in there? Look!"

Before he could say more, fright banished all thought,
for a crash sounded from inside the building—sparks flew
high—burning pieces of wood were thrown around. Something had collapsed, and it was impossible to help Johnny
now—

Johnny had rushed in through the barracks, toward
the door on the right leading to Mabel's own room. He
was compelled to stop a moment in the doorway to locate
himself and accustom his eyes to the fog of smoke. Here
in this room they had tried to provide a little more of
civilization. Here she had sat—this woman from the
States—and here in this room he had seemed to find all
the world outside the polar regions—here, where she filled
the room with her warmth and charm. He saw the flames
lick up the rose-colored curtains—her furniture was afire

—and the lovely mirror which he himself, at the cost of much labor, had brought up from Cape King on his sled— that, too, was cracked and twisted, and its frame now a fiery border around the glass.

He was recalled from his thoughts by a pain in his hand. The fire had touched him. Now he remembered his errand. There on her desk stood the little box. He saw the flames lick at it, but he managed to open it. His finger tips stung with the heat. And there were the two bundles of letters. They were beginning to smolder, but he seized them. The silk ribbon about one bundle had burned in two, and the paper corners were already charred brown. "Your devoted Markmann," was written across one corner. He couldn't help but see it. The envelope was burned at the edges and the paper had curled up so he couldn't help but see the writing.

"Your devoted Markmann."

The name was strange to him. Ah, some letters that must be saved! He could think no more, for the confusion in his brain. Crashes and buzzing! He was overcome by the smoke, and the ceiling seemed to slip down on him. Whichever way he struggled forward, he met fire. He remembered once to smother the flames on the bundles of letters. He tried to struggle on, but sensed that he was falling, and tried to raise himself to crawl. A sudden sharp pain in his knee, and then he remembered no more . . .

He lay in the snow, gasping for breath. It was Godthardt, the old Indian, who bent over him—Godthardt, who for many years had cooked for the police. When Mabel had screamed, the cook had rushed into the building—and managed to get far enough so he could grab Johnny and drag him out of the flames.

Mabel and Frank knelt beside Johnny.

"He's coming to," said Mabel. "Come, Frank, let's carry him away—down to the supply-house. It will be better there than here with the Indians. Take hold of him so." And they lifted him up. But Johnny felt life returning to him.

"I can walk," he said, leaning against Mabel. "See, here are your letters."

"Oh, the letters," said Mabel. "I'd forgotten them. But you got them—thanks!" She seized the two small bundles with scorched corners, and shoved them into her pocket.

Strange sights in the supply-house. It was a good thing that Johnny had always had enough foresight to keep plenty of reserve provisions and clothing stored there, away from the barracks. They built an oven and were fairly comfortable. By using boards from packing boxes, they partitioned off a little room where they ate and slept and crept together about the oven. Frank was a jack-of-all-trades. From the supplies in the storehouse he rigged up a radio. He made his own loudspeaker, and the monotonous life in these small quarters—without books or anything else to pass the time—was made easier by contact with the outside world.

Now the long day was about to begin. Mabel suffered a great deal from the cramped quarters and severe living conditions; it was decided that Frank should take her by sled to Cape King, and from there she should travel to Cape McKensey, and stay there until the ice broke up. Then Johnny could either go to get her or move down there himself.

At the same time, Frank would take out the mail, so

the inspector could be notified that the house had burned, but that the station was still taken care of.

Johnny would stay and keep an eye on his district. The other two constables had gone on a trip long before the fire. They must have arrived at the inspector's quarters now—were perhaps on their way back again.

Johnny was to be alone at the station—and such a primitive station—after Mabel left with Frank. It didn't appeal much to Johnny. They packed her things, and toward evening, the last before they set out, Johnny saw her take the packets of letters, which now were neatly arranged and tied with twine. It was obvious they had been read since he saved them from the fire.

"Mabel," he said, "I brought you those letters out of the fire. Tell me what they are."

"Oh Johnny," she said, looking at him.

"Oh well, I won't ask if you don't want to tell me—but who is Markmann?"

"What? Have you read my letters? I've never mentioned that name. Oh, Johnny, Johnny, can't I trust you?"

He sprang up, and stared at his wife.

"Mabel—you don't believe—Mabel, that night when I stood in your room for the last time, with the fire around me, I had your letters in my hand. The outside paper was burned off, and the others curled up from the heat. I happened to see the word 'Markmann.' But no—" he interrupted himself. "I don't want to defend myself, for you can't believe—oh, Mabel—you leave tomorrow!"

They clasped hands and gazed at each other with a look which said that their farewell hour must not be degraded by mistrust by either of them.

Johnny was alone. Indians came and Indians went again. The chief of the station never passed a day in which he was not concerned with the welfare of the natives. But when night came, he was alone, so alone! At 8 P.M. he heard the *Press,* the newspaper that told the lonely polar dweller what was happening in the world—events in which he might not share.

"Hello, hello. Radio news. Revolution in Spain—Robbery in New York that amazed everyone—Murderer from Edmonton captured—Results of the prize fight . . ."

But one night he heard something different.

"News has come to McKensey from the central broadcasting station. The police barracks at Lake Caribou has burned down. John Barthold and his wife were saved with difficulty. Mrs. Barthold has traveled over west, and there met another traveler, Markmann Hurley, who brought her safely to Cape McKensey. Mr. Hurley was on his way up to visit Mrs. Barthold, but they met each other on the trail near Cape King."

Johnny was amazed. Markmann Hurley. He searched his memory for the name. No, he didn't know it. Markmann. But that was the name in the letter. "Your devoted Markmann." Who was he? So it was his letters which *must* be saved, whatever the cost! A man on his way up to get Mabel! Johnny feared for his reason.

True enough, he and Mabel had met up here on the Alaskan border, when she was alone with her father's body.

He had protected her from gold miners who had found her sitting by her sled with her dying father. Mabel told him her life story. Oh no, who can tell that? And how much of it was true—how much forgotten and how much concealed? All lies, naturally. Letters from Markmann! He looked at his hand, which bore the scars of the severe burns. And it was these bits of letters from him—that man —whom he felt he could murder in cold blood. His letters were worth the risk of Johnny's life.

The days went by, and with them went all of Johnny's spirits. His longing for Mabel became a clamoring desire—sometimes almost hate. Sometimes he said to himself, "Oh, no, it's impossible. Mabel's not like that—she *can't* be like that, after our three years together. Why should she choose me—I brought her nothing but the safety I was duty-bound to offer her? Why should she stay here with me?"

He brooded and brooded. But Mabel was gone. Every evening he listened to the cold, impersonal radio—but no news of Mabel. It's hell to live in the ice wastes with only a half-knowledge of a thing, and no way to learn more about it.

Dogs barking—then Frank appeared out of the snowstorm. Johnny sprang up. This time no "Hello—glad to see you!" This time no laughter and shouts of welcome. No, Johnny grabbed him and pulled him into the supply-house, to light and warmth.

"Frank, where's Mabel? Who was it she went away with? Where did you meet him? What way did she go? Have you got a letter for me?"

One question after the other hurled at the newcomer.

"Johnny, be quiet," said Frank, for he knew this was a serious matter. "I've got a letter from Mabel. She traveled west with the stranger, a man who was on his way up here, and who explained the situation. He agreed with me that he'd better not travel further, but settle his business. It was something that concerned your wife."

"Business!" said Johnny. "Who's she got business with? What man in the world has dealings with her that I'm not to know about?"

"Well, read your letter," said Frank. He almost had to struggle with Johnny to get outside and bring in the mail sack. It was emptied out on the table, and Johnny pawed the letters over. He snatched one. He knew the writing, and tore the envelope open. Frank stood looking at him questioningly. He saw that Johnny sensed nothing about him—he was lost in his letter.

The old Indian cook brought food. "Tea is ready."

But Johnny heard nothing.

"Hello, Chief," said the cook again.

Johnny looked up from his letter.

"Let Mr. Frank eat alone. I'm not hungry," he said, and continued reading. When he'd finished the letter, he put it into his vest pocket and sat down to brood—staring straight before him. It wasn't a cheerful evening, Frank's first night home. No answer to any question—not a look from Johnny. The place was dismal, and Frank was tired.

"Goodnight," he said after a few hours. "I've traveled a long way today and I'm going to bed."

No answer. Johnny sat as he'd been sitting all evening —his fingers drumming nervously on the table—staring before him—sensing nothing.

"Frank," said Johnny next morning, "I'm leaving!"

"What?" said Frank. "What're you going to do?"

"I'm leaving," said Johnny. "I'm going over west. Here

Peter Freuchen and Knud Rasmussen, 1913

Kasaluk, Navarana's mother, with her small children

An Eskimo boy, Hudson Bay

Mountains on the Greenland coast

Ice floes in a Greenland bay

Reindeer round up in Lapland
(Finnish National Tourist Office

Eskimo family in tent (Canadian National Film Board photograph)

The *Danmark,* bark used
in arctic exploration

A walrus hunter with seal bladder attached to his harpoon

Eskimo wedding party in Thule, Greenland

Knud Rasmussen among Eskimos in Thule. In the foreground is one-eyed Merqusaq, Navarana's grandfather

The harbor road at Egedesminde, Greenland (Royal Danish Ministry of Foreign Affairs)

In a Hudson Bay store (National Film Board of Canada)

On the way to market
in Lapland

Eskimo drying rack (Alaska Airlines photo)

The Pangnirtung parka, large enough to hold a small child in its hood (National Film Board of Canada)

Eskimo reindeer, domesticated caribou, in the Far North
(Alaska Airlines photo)

The monument to Knud
Rasmussen in Greenland

Cleansing and gutting a seal

Lake Baikal in Siberia

Rafting logs down one of the rivers into Lake Baikal

Peter Freuchen among friends near Mount Umanak, Thule, Greenland

Eskimos spinning over in their kayaks

Two Lapps and a reindeer (Finnish Tourist Association)

Godthaab, Greenland

Mail arriving at a Royal Canadian Mounted Police post in the Far North
(National Film Board of Canada)

A large ice cave on Greenland's East Coast

The ice wall, 180 feet high, showing striations, around Ymers Nunatak, 1908

A Hudson Bay Eskimo

Snow houses built during the First Thule Expedition, 1911

are the records and the police reports, and you can write in them that on this date staff sergeant Barthold left his post without reason, thereby neglecting his duties."

"Sergeant, what in the world are you talking about? Of course I'll not write any such thing."

"Okay, Frank," was the answer. "I'm going after my wife. She's gone, but I suppose she can be found. Her letter only tells me that she's met a man she's been expecting for a long time, and she asks me to wait for her until she comes back, even if it is a long time. Frank, last night taught me more than I've learned in all my life before! Stay here in the ice fields, with the Indians on the edge of the forest, and wait and wait—even if it is a long time! No, Frank, I'm leaving!"

Johnny wasn't a man to be easily opposed. Everyone knew he was very strong-willed. Frank saw him put two revolvers in his pockets. He saw Johnny hitch his dogs to the sled and pack his baggage. And when he'd put on his snowshoes, he started the sled on its way. Sludge, sludge came the sound, and Frank saw him vanish between the trees in the distance.

Traveling alone allows ample time for much thinking. Johnny was alone. When his dogs wanted to rest a while by going more slowly, his whip fell on them unrelentingly. He increased his speed toward night, rather than slow up, and his dogs had to keep up with him, for his whip was merciless and it bit flesh every time it fell.

When he reached Cape King, he hadn't slept much. Only when his dogs fell from sheer exhaustion did he let them rest while he lit a fire and sat staring into the flames. Once in a while, when his body became too tired to keep going, he fell over in a deep sleep until the fire burned out and the cold wakened him again. Then he was on his feet at once, forcing his dogs to go on.

No festivities during his visit at Cape King. The old staff sergeant was very fond of his colleague, and was glad to see him, but when Johnny entered the room, his face showed what his thoughts were, and the old sergeant knew that something had happened that wouldn't bear words. They spoke only of necessary things. Lonely folk know all about deep thoughts, and know that he who is uneasy in his own mind must not be bothered by useless talk from others. Johnny ate—he slept in the station's camp bed, and next morning he felt rested and thought only of going farther.

Sludge, sludge! After a few days had passed, he heard the sound of his own snowshoes. He was thought out. What he intended to say and do, he had no idea, but he felt the urge to travel farther. Now he obeyed this urge almost unconsciously—like a slave driven by a force not to be withstood.

He had learned at Cape King that a strange man and his wife had traveled over west. He'd surely meet them in McKensey, because a woman can't travel very fast, and they weren't set on making time. They were only concerned with getting there, but no one knew why. Johnny heard that Mr. Hurley was a young, active man—a sportsman, but not accustomed to life in the north. The old sergeant sought to pacify Johnny regarding his wife.

"They are old friends. He'll take care of her, and see that she's all right. You needn't worry—nothing will happen to her."

These words had calmed the alarmed husband, but

now that he was on the trail again, he read a new meaning
into the words, and rage grew in him. Then his rage
turned to cold hatred, and now all that mattered was to
go forward—forward, and what might follow would be
as fate willed it.

A sled-trail in northern Canada is a track made by the
first traveler along the way, and followed by all later
comers. So Johnny drove his team out from the forests,
up into the treeless wastes, and the dogs followed the way
of their own accord. All he needed to do was to use the
whip to keep them going to full speed.

And so it happened one night that he stumbled upon
those he sought. A camp alongside the trail, with dogs
around the tents, with people and fires. He saw it from
far off, but thought of nothing more definite than that
he must go forward—forward, and so he reached their
camp. He sprang from his sled, letting the Indians care
for the dogs. He tore open the tent door and stepped forward into the light. There they were! His wife, Mabel,
with smiling face. She stopped in the midst of a story—her
laughter stiffened to fear.

"Johnny!" she cried, half-rising, but held back by his
look.

Beside her lounged two men, comfortably stretched
out on soft deerskins while they listened to the woman.
And although Johnny had worked himself up into an
almost insane rage, such a feeling of well-being and peace
and innocence met him that it couldn't help but affect
him.

"Mabel," he said, "you left me—and who went with
you? Mabel, I've come to get you."

"Yes, but Johnny! Johnny! What makes you look like

that? Why did you come here? Oh, my sweetheart! Listen, Johnny . . ."

But he pushed her away.

"Mabel, explain yourself. Who is this man? Who is it the radio mentioned—the man of the letters? Tell me that, Mabel, or else . . ." He didn't finish, but stuck his hand in his pocket, and the handle of a revolver showed in his fist.

"Johnny!" cried Mabel.

The other man sprang to his feet.

"Mr. Barthold, I presume?" he said. "I'm glad to meet you. I came for Mabel, and I happened to meet her and took her back with me to prove certain matters to her."

"Is my wife Mabel to you?" asked Johnny harshly. "Who are you? I want the truth. For three years I've known that my wife kept secrets from me, and now I want things explained, or else one of us is going to die."

He was interrupted by Mabel, who sprang up, threw her arms about his neck, and pressed her face close to his.

"Oh, Johnny, Johnny, what are you saying? You couldn't believe . . . Oh, Johnny, how could you?"

This was really no explanation—but the tones of her voice were more than enough. They told him that she was innocent of any wrong.

Now Mr. Hurley took command of the situation.

"Mr. Barthold, Mabel has told me all about her life up here, and about you, too. I'll admit that when we heard that Mabel had married a policeman we were none too pleased. My name is Markmann Hurley. I'm Mabel's cousin, and she and I share in a fortune. It was this fortune that her father left behind in his anger. My father was married to his sister, but there was hate between the two men, and Mabel's father, who had a proud nature, left without defending himself when he was falsely accused. But he's dead now, and others are dead who had helped to part the family. So when my father became ill, I promised him I'd find my cousin and give her what was rightly hers. And I'll tell you, Sergeant, if you want to do what's best for your wife—and for you, too—you'll end this arctic adventure. After all she's told me, I don't believe she's lost anything by spending three years here, and she's found herself a husband, too. If you have even half of the good qualities she's endowed you with, I'll welcome you into our firm right now, for you're the kind of a man my company can use."

Johnny had the queerest sensations through his body. He seemed weak in the knees—and his arms were without strength. Something like tears clouded his vision, but the only thing he sensed was shame—and he sank down on the pelt-covered pallet—totally unable to speak coherently.

"Mabel, little Mabel," was all he could stammer, and his hand sought to touch her. She took his hand and kissed it.

"This wonderfully big, strong hand," she said "the hand you burned full of scars when I asked you to get my letters. They were the evidence of my father's rights— and mine, too. I was afraid of losing them—not on my account, for I had you anyway, but because I wanted you to enjoy some of all the good things here in the world, which you have so richly deserved."

5.

The Big Teacher

THE SUN IS SHINING. There is not wind enough to blow out a match. The water between the ice cakes looks like oil, and there is no sound to interrupt the calmness of the arctic sea. If it weren't for the huge barrier of ice up north, the *Viking* certainly would have been plowing ahead. But the captain saw from his crow's-nest that it was impossible.

Nothing is as necessary as patience in the Far North. The captain knew that. But in a big whaler you have to keep your crew busy. They are men from every place in the world—some from bad places. Whaling is not for weak ones. No sportsmanship, no gallant fight with game. Only pull or be damned, as the boys say.

Still the same men go out year after year. They curse it from the day the ship goes out until it comes home. Then there are some few gay days in the restaurants and bars around the harbor—days of liquor, nights of all sorts of foolishness.

Some spend the winter after that in starvation and freezing. They have no friends, no home. They are kicked from place to place when their money is gone. So when the whalers make ready the next time, the boys are just tired to misery and glad to get out again.

Whenever an oldtimer brings a new hand along for whaling, you can expect the fellow to be hard up. That was Satumen. He was worse than the men had ever seen before. He had just got out of prison. His last rap was for two years. And next time he would be in for a lot longer—ten to twenty. He knew the process.

But Satumen realized when it was too late. He didn't want to start going straight at his age—why should a man change when he's made a name for himself? And his friends were like him, guys who fought police and law in every way. A break-in or a hold-up gave them the dough they wanted. But still they played safe, they believed in taking precautions. It was a tough life, but it was still better than working.

Work was what you had to do in jail, and Satumen did enough to learn to hate it. He couldn't bear the thought of having ten to twenty years full of the same in the basket for him. But it was too late to undo the robbery now. The only thing to do was to lay low and keep away from the cops.

And so his friend brought him down to the *Viking* and he was hired. The mate knew the story but he didn't care. He received so much commission for each man he got on the ship, and those without papers could never complain at the end of the trip about the treatment they got. Satumen was kept below decks until the ship was out of the harbor. There were four more of his kind down there with him, just taking life easy. They thought they were going to have a little vacation at sea—something to brag about later.

But the mates were able to make any man work, even someone like Satumen. And what they couldn't do, the crew could. This is not to speak of the skipper—he was worse than the rest of the officers put together, and then some.

So Satumen was taught how to scrub a deck. He was put on the tools that needed sharpening. Then the ropes were gone over. Never a moment to himself. The coal had to be shifted from the hold up on deck down to the bunkers. Wood had to be carried. And all the while he suffered from seasickness. Being sick did not release a man from duty on the *Viking*. It only brought him some kicks in the backside from the mates, if he lacked speed enough to get away in time. Satumen protested a couple of times, only to be knocked down and told to hurry up and make up for the time wasted by the scrap.

Satumen began regretting this way of life. The jail had its routine, and one had to put up with all kinds of foolishness it was true, but one had his sleep, food in abundance, and there were rules about how to talk to prisoners. Here on the *Viking* there was only slavery. Rotten food, curses, and beatings every hour in the day, meals to be eaten in no time—then out on deck again right away.

Satumen was so tired he could die. He thought of the guy who got him into all this. He knew he got his commission for every man and he began to hate him. He wanted to kill him! But he didn't have the guts to fight him. He was tamed while on the *Viking* and the only idea in his sea-broken brain was to get on shore. He wanted to feel the holy earth under his feet again.

But now they reached the ice. Nothing is a nicer change. The never-resting ground swell that had ripped Satumen's stomach and hollowed his cheeks was gone. The huge waves disappeared.

When you get inside the polar ice, smooth water lies before you. Birds fly around. Seals poke their heads up over the surface. Some of them even sleep on the ice in the sun. Everything is peaceful, and nature seems to welcome visitors.

But Satumen soon saw that the politics of the north was different than its nature. The captain was ingenious at keeping his crew busy. He had to be. If they had time to rest they would find fault with the food, kick about the work, protest against his treatment. The officers had to handle them roughly and keep them aware that while they were aboard they didn't even have the privilege to suggest anything. If a guy started fooling around the first thing to do was to show him that the hell he learned about in school was a Sunday's rest compared with what was in store for him here.

Only in this way could the discipline of the *Viking* be kept up—the discipline of the good ship *Viking*.

A cry from the crow's-nest informed the skipper that something was sighted. "Ship ahoy!" was called. Everybody listened.

A ship was seen making its way right down on the *Viking*.

The captain discussed it with his mates. There was no whaling ship up here that they knew of. When it came closer it was seen to be smaller than a whaler, and when it came closer still, they saw how bad conditions were on board.

The *Lark* had been out for the worst the Far North can offer—gales from the time she left home, disaster during the whole trip. Two boats lost and several men. They were short of hands. Their miserable state could not be hidden. The owner, Ross Bingley asked for help. The two captains had met before, so they went below to talk it over. The result was that four men and some needed supplies were to be transferred to the *Lark*. This was one of the most annoying times in a whaling captain's life. He had to ask for volunteers. He was responsible for all of them. The men were signed only for his ship, so everything had to be done properly. He couldn't force anyone to take leave and go over to another ship unless some danger demanded it.

Of course he had a couple of boys not exactly registered, but he hated to admit it to Ross Bingley, who was known as a churchman. But he managed to put forward his request and get four men asking to go with the *Lark*. Among them naturally was Satumen, to whom any change seemed bound to be for the better.

When ships separate from each other in the Arctic Ocean, one always has a feeling of solemnity. Everybody is on deck; there are shouts of Good-by, and Good Luck! The ships move slowly through the ice, then separate, and a feeling of desolation comes over you when only the ice can be seen for miles around. But soon the mates bellow the dreamers back to work, curses and orders bring them to the jobs and make them forget they are alone, and the day goes on.

The *Lark* was very different from the *Viking*. Ross Bingley was a trader running three separate stores for the Eskimos way up north. Right now he was heading for the farthest one to supply his port there with trading material and goods.

He had endured severe losses to get this far, but it was still early in the season. Now that he had these four new men nothing seemed to block him from going ahead.

Satumen got an impression of weakness from Bingley because of his pleasant way of talking with the mate, and also with the crew. Everybody liked to chat with him. So Satumen rather quickly invented a story about being kidnaped and shanghaied by the whalers; he used to be a storekeeper and had taken a trip to town where he was quickly jumped and carried away. Ross felt sorry for him, but explained that he would have to take his watches just the same, at least for the present. He explained how he needed the men he got from the whaler, couldn't get through without their help. Satumen said, sure, he wanted to work, but he was worried the men might dislike him if he did not keep up to them on the job, and just wanted to offer an explanation ahead of time.

Satumen of course hated the *Lark*, he was disgusted with the whole thing, but what was he to do? The monotony of the ship was getting him, so he faked being sick, whereupon the captain himself came and took care of him. Lying in his bunk Satumen felt much better and he intended to stay there for the rest of the trip. He was quite comfortable in the horizontal position.

For many days the towering mountains had been in view, reaching into the clouds, or capped with snow. The midnight sun had shown them the beauty of the north, and soon they would be at their destination. In his bunk Satumen could take a look out through the bull's-eye. He was surprised to discover that all his worries were forgotten in looking out at the scenery and those wonderful colors. But he quickly scolded himself for being sentimental—the whole point was to get home as quickly as possible and then horn in on something on shore.

But his meditations were interrupted by the ship's arrival at port. There was a shout from somebody on deck.

All the men were happy and he heard the fellows talking of the small Eskimos and their fun. But he was sick and couldn't go out!

So he spat on the floor with disgust and turned his back on the world and lay down, trying to get some sleep before supper.

But it was impossible; sailors came running in to tell about the houses and how everyone was enjoying himself. Most of them had sailed here for years and were friends of the natives and the white men on shore. Even now, when they came with bad news, having lost people on the way up, it was still evident that the isolated little world was delighted to see them. There were letters for the whites, provisions for the natives. The little village was full of laughter, the faces of the people were like an eternal smile from ear to ear.

A man was sick in the forecastle, the people heard, and many of them came in to try and cheer him up. Normally Satumen would have chased them out. But he was curious after the long trip at sea so he let them stay. Two men came close to him and tried to make themselves understood.

"You no good feel?" they asked him and changed over to their native tongue which sounded like cough and sneeze to him. One of them handed him a piece of ivory carved in the shape of a polar bear. This was the first time in Satumen's life that he had a friendly gesture from an unknown person. Before he could accustom himself to it, they ran out of the cabin and he heard them talking and laughing outside. Soon others came in to see him, and everybody gave him a little thing. They felt sorry that he was ill. They tried to make him understand that the big annual feast on shore, held every time the ship arrived, was something terrible to miss. He did not have the nerve to tell them to go to hell. They ran in and ran out like children, with no thought of bothering him, just anxious to show their sympathy.

In the afternoon after work had stopped, his shipmates went ashore. The summer night's dance began in the open, on the beach. Satumen could hear everyone shouting and laughing and screaming with joy. He felt envious, but he realized that he was made of another kind of stuff; only he got mad over the noise and got no sleep.

When they came on board he gave them hell, but they just told him to shut up. You don't know how to sail in these waters, up here we are all alike and every night is dance and fun. You will see after we are homebound how tired you can be. You have to sleep the whole free watch to make it up.

Satumen understood that he was outvoted. He just wondered how white people could lower themselves to this, and he told them so. But every man in the forecastle went against him for it, and so his first experience in the arctic was not pleasant.

Two days went by. Satumen had decided to stay in bed for the rest of the trip. The captain came every day and saw him, but he complained and moaned—there was pain all over and no strength at all.

But in the evening when he heard the frolicking on shore, and when they came back on board and talked about the dances and the good treatment they got, when he saw the eyes shining in all the boys, he was filled with regret. His hate for the men grew with their happiness.

An old sailor had his money lying open in his sea chest. Now was the time for taking it, Satumen realized. But he had to get out of the ship, of course. If he were the only man below, there was no chance for him.

But that meant recovering, and after that, work. So no, thanks! Still the thought was in him.

The women were not allowed on board, only the men could come and visit as they wanted. But they all brought small gifts from the girls on shore, who had heard of the sick man in bed. They pitied him: "While we are having fun, he is tortured with pain."

"Quite some decent people, however," Satumen couldn't help thinking.

Soon, they went to sea again. Satumen changed his politics. His restoration to health began slowly. Very slowly, of course.

But he sat up; he came out on deck and claimed to be able to sit in the sun and get fresh air. Ross Bingley, a strong man with health like a bull, believed him to be doing his best and encouraged him as best he could.

He even showed up with a drink of brandy to make strength. With that Satumen felt life was not so bad after all.

At the next place he felt strong enough to go on shore and watch the dance. Unfortunately he could not join it. It would look too suspicious. But the girls came and smiled at him, the elderly women brought him a pair of mittens, and the children picked berries. At night when he was on board the ship again he decided to recover quickly and then get a new spell on the way home.

Next morning Captain Ross called on him, asking about

his health. "Not good, but somewhat better," he answered. "I only wish I had some strength; I do not like to see the boys doing my work too."

"Oh, that's all right, but don't you think you could go in a boat and supervise some girls rowing out after some narwhal skins left out on the point? We have to have those skins, and it will take a man from unloading if you can't go."

Satumen went. He had just to sit and keep the tiller in his hand. Six girls did the rowing. On the cape they built a fire and cooked meat and made coffee. Never in his life had Satumen felt like this. He was brought up in a big city. There had been no parents, no friendship for him. Man against man, hand against hand, that was his experience. But here in the arctic sun, six girls, all of them laughing and playing, healthy and gay and kind to each other. He began to see his own life in a new light. The food tasted better than he could have imagined. He caressed one of the girls and she became very tender under his hand. The rest of them just smiled and looked kindly at him. They joked with him that his sickness would disappear rather soon. They all liked him and one of them stayed by him while the rest of them loaded the skins from the cache.

Aninak went after water for him. She collected some flowers from the nearby hills, she threw more driftwood on the fire, and she made him comfortable on all their coats. She told him in broken English to relax, and a new feeling came over his soul.

Flowers in the arctic were a surprise to him, and sweetness from a girl was something he had never thought of.

Aninak made him understand that she was to come along in the *Lark* to the next place with her father, who knew the words of the white men.

On their way back Satumen had the feeling that he should take the oar from Aninak and row. But he came to his senses and realized he was a sick man and that work was against his beliefs. So he enjoyed the scenery.

Icebergs produced all kinds of color above and below the water. The sun sent its rays into their eyes. Birds by the thousands flew or swam. They dived down and came up as if they were shot out of a gun down below. The mountains framed this beautiful picture. And even if the ice floated around, the temperature was warm and everything induced happiness and joy. The girls sang as they rowed. With each stroke their bodies raised, then sank down again. Often they saw something unusual and Satumen liked this. It took the attention of the others from him and his girl.

Then they stopped and talked. They enjoyed themselves, they laughed and shouted. But Satumen got impatient and told them to keep on. "Stick to your jobs and let's keep going. To hell with the birds and the seals, hurry up and step on it."

They got scared and their smiles disappeared for a moment. They talked with low voices "Sick man pain," said Aninak to him, "many hurry."

They hurried on for a short time, but soon they forgot again and the trip became a picnic as before. That trip made Satumen well. He decided to go to work, so he could attend the dance in the evening.

He walked in the hills with Aninak and realized that things were different. Never had he cared for animals before, never for the beauty of the land. The girl made him dream, and the natives with their smiles affected him more than he could admit.

Aninak and her father, the old man Samik, followed to the next place, which was the last they were going to visit.

Here the conditions were bad. The trader had died; his house was closed. The natives came out, sorrow on their faces. This is their etiquette. But soon everyone saw their old smiles. "We are happy to be rescued and get opportunity to trade again."

They had closed the store and not touched a thing after the trader's death. "We did not know the value, so we could not replace it with skins or ivory."

Ross Bingley looked things over. There was not a needle missing; everything was in place. But the natives, of course, were in need of goods, so the trading went on at once.

Satumen helped Bingley trading. He had told his story of being a store man at home, so he was naturally picked for this job. And he had ability to do the job rather well; what he didn't know, he explained away by saying how different things were up here. He told Bingley how cleverly everything was handled, and how he admired the way the natives lived, and so on.

Gradually Satumen got the idea of staying here. Where in the world could he hide like here? Nothing to do but hand out some things to those good-natured natives, whom he was beginning to enjoy. The nice girl Aninak was on his mind all the time, and after all he could go home after a year. Having been out of the way, he was sure nobody would recognize him. And he would not be the man he was if he could make a good deal out of it some way.

So he filed his application for staying. Ross Bingley had not much hesitation. Somebody had to do it. He had an old sailor, who used to live up here, but he was not able to count on him. Satumen had picked up valuable knowledge—that he got it in jail he did not say. So he was given a farewell dinner on board the last day. He was instructed to the last detail and then he went on shore as the *Lark* departed.

Satumen, the crook, the burglar and robber, was now the teacher of primitive people. A strange feeling came over him as he landed. He realized he had been just crazy. Where had his good sense gone? Here he was—in desolation beyond any place in the world. He had heard about connections by sledges in winter with the other posts, but he now realized for the first time that he was cut off. He had been a fool, a child; like a schoolboy he had fancied adventure and excitement where there was only desolation. He had a great temptation to hurry away, but he had waited too long.

The natives came to him and asked where to take his belongings. Samik the old interpreter asked him twice.

"Shut up and keep quiet," he snarled. Samik told the others that the white man was full of thoughts on seeing his countrymen leaving on the dangerous voyage home. He, who was safe, now felt sorry for them. So he shouldn't be disturbed.

But at that moment the *Lark* gave a salute. She let her whistle blow, and the tone rolled over the fjord and far inland. Between the mountains standing proud in the air, the sound penetrated every valley and cleft, and back it came. The silent north gave back the farewell to the foreigners going away. Echo after echo answered, but this was too much for Satumen.

He would not stay up here. It was never his intention, it was only a joke—a bad one. Should a man who got away from ten to twenty years give himself up in snow and ice and lose what he gained—freedom to do what he pleased, freedom to do a big job, to snap up easy money wholesale? No, not him!

So he ran for the ship, but it was not possible to reach it in the little boat, he saw that. Then he realized that the sound was carried from a long distance to where he was. So he ran for the flagstaff. He yelled and screamed and swung his cap and cried his fear out to the ship:

"*Lark* ahoy! *Lark* ahoy! Come back! Come back! I won't stay here! It's a lie! It's a big lie! I want to go home! I want to go home!"

Ross Bingley saw him waving and he heard his voice. "He is bidding us good-by. Fine boy! Dip the flag three times for him."

Satumen kept on yelling, "Take me home, take me home, take me to jail! I will not stay up here! I will not! *Lark* ahoy!"

His voice cracked from screaming. The flag on the *Lark* went down and up in his honor, and then the ship disappeared round the cape and set the course for the long return voyage, loaded with arctic goods, and eager to lay up until next season.

Satumen saw it disappear. Never in his life had he been so sorry. He remembered the first time the jailer closed the bars after him. But it hadn't been so bad as this. There were other prisoners in the jail, and he could at least show them he was a real fellow; but here he was alone. Alone and nobody to talk to! He had not given the winter a single thought. Now he knew for the first time in his life what it was to be alone.

Up in the arctic everybody has to watch himself, or else he'll live a short time. And Satumen was afraid to die, terribly afraid to die.

He felt his legs giving way, he fell down like a bunch of rope and stayed there in anguish, without a thought in his head except for the ship that had left, the sailors he could no longer speak to. He regretted not being able to work with them; he sobbed like a kid. Nothing was left of the tough guy who had no feeling for anybody.

An Eskimo near him asked what was going on. But he heard his sobbing, he saw his tears running, and realized that no other man had any business here. So he went back to the other tribesmen and gave them his observations:

"Our new trader is a witch-doctor; an angakok has come to us. He is talking to his spirits to manage a safe voyage for his friends. He is on the safe side himself, he got the best part of it, being able to stay up here, but he wants to use all the strength he has in our favored country to compel the spirit to give his friends safe return.

"This shows us that our trader is kind and thinks of other folks. Let us feel happy that he arrived and will stay with us."

How long Satumen lay there he did not know himself. No hope, no desire, nothing was left in the man who walked slowly down the little hill. He directed his steps toward the house, and the natives moved away as he passed by. They felt humble before the man who had just been in contact with the spirits, who control everything in the world.

Satumen went inside. He saw an almost empty house.

Furniture that was not real furniture. A table with paper he was supposed to write on, the books to be kept. He laughed. No books would be kept, he was going to burn them. He wasn't going to do any trading. He had to stay here, but more than this year nobody would be able to keep him. He almost laughed to think that his boss had hired him for three years.

Satumen looked with real terror on the days to come. Two dogs howled outside. Their voices echoed his own feelings—no hope, no words, just sorrow and despair. He listened for a while, then he grabbed a stick and ran out of the house. The dogs were held with heavy chains. They belonged to the station. They were his animals to haul him around in winter and bring ice and coal to his house. Now they just sat there and howled in the deathly silence, poking their heads up in the air.

Satumen swung his stick; the dogs got frightened and tried to avoid the blows by jumping from side to side. He got entangled in their chains and fell, but he kept on beating the poor beasts. It was as if his own misery were eased by inflicting whatever pain he could on the animals.

In the head and along their flanks, the blood streamed down the skin, but he never stopped. He kicked them with his boots and he smashed them with his stick. Finally the dogs understood that he was a madman, there was no mercy to be expected! They submitted to the punishment and just crumpled together, while he kept on.

But the satisfaction was gone, so he threw his stick away and stopped.

The natives stood aside and looked at him. No Eskimo will interfere when a man handles his dogs, no matter what he does. That is up to the owner.

"Here is a man that takes interest in dogs," said old

Qilerneq. "He want them to know from the beginning that he is the master. That will save him from whipping them later on. A man that thinks is among us!"

The natives went home and told their wives that this winter they were going to see dog training such as they never believed possible. "Our much-knowing trader will teach us!"

A man was called Orsulik. He was the hired man of the post, and he had been at it for years. The late trader used to be patient with him, for he was not what we would call an expert in doing service. A hunter without great success, he had made a habit of staying home and watching the white man. But a post manager is interested in keeping everybody active; he must have skins and he can't have people hanging around.

Orsulik was not highly esteemed by the tribe, no great fame was connected with his years, but he was friendly and well liked. He was accepted as a man who did not hunt himself; his duty was to make life easier for the white man whose years were few up here. So he was to be looked after like a newborn baby in this country.

Orsulik entered the house. A fire had to be lit in the stove, good wishes could be expected from the mouth of the trader.

He was greeted with a blow in his face. He was startled for a moment, then he received another shock— this time on his forehead. Satumen went wild. The poor Orsulik was beaten beyond belief. He fell down and was jerked up again; he was knocked unconscious and was brought to. He felt the punches in his ribs and the slaps on his cheeks. A man was beating him without reason. Satumen had to do something to release himself from the terrible pain. He spat at the Eskimo and hit him until his hands hurt. Then he kicked him some more, but finally his muscles gave way. He could do no more to the man. He hardly had the strength to pull him, limp as he was, to the door and throw him out.

Orsulik felt the blows but his surprise made him passive. He was beaten, but what for? He was no fighter, no Eskimo is, but even at that he could not resist asking, For what reason?

There was no hate between them, he had greeted the new man in a friendly way, and they had worked together as long as the ship was there. Some unknown reason must be behind all this. Can a man resist what he does not understand?

Crying with pain and bleeding from his nose and mouth, and with loose teeth and hurting limbs, he walked down to the tents and told his strange story. The older folks began to think. Something extraordinary had happened, but nobody dared judge too soon. But the old man Qilerneq knew. The wisdom of their forefathers was in his old skull. So he explained:

"Here we have a man that does not know our language too well. He is without means of telling us his intentions. But he wants to show us his unexpected strength. What a lucky thing for us! We see what help we can have from our trader against the difficulties that fill our lives. Let us be happy for the mighty man we have as a settler among us. He could do this even without anger, how will he be against our enemies if they come along? Orsulik has had to suffer some, but are our days ever without difficulties? Pain is only annoying as long as it lasts. A big teacher is among us."

The evening brought an appetite to Satumen. For the first time he realized what it was to make his own food, do his own housekeeping. He had heard about pioneers, but it had never occurred to him that he would be one himself some day.

But he put off his hunger until late. Then he took some bread they had given him from the ship, and opened a can of food. His spirits were low, he felt miserable, and the coming days would be just like this. Just like this!

The next day he saw Orsulik come to his house—a bit nervously—but he had no feeling of guilt. Satumen made no remark about yesterday. The routine went on, the house was put in order. It was quite cold, the fall set in, and Satumen got a visit from Samik, the interpreter. He was told about what to do and how to do it.

Winter was sure to be bad and preparations were to be made. In the place of company he could talk to, he had to deal with the natives, and he already knew Samik and his daughter, Aninak. The girl was to be married to a young fellow as soon as the ice formed. He was living in another settlement close by, and as soon as dogs could drag a sledge on the fjord he was bound to arrive. Satumen liked the girl and he had a notion not to let any guy get away with her.

With the winter coming he had to have Eskimo clothes, old Samik told him.

"Let somebody sew them for me," he said, and a few days later a handsome garment lay before him. Two old women brought it to him and watched him try it on. They stayed for a while and expected payment for the work. But Satumen had his bad temper on, and he felt offended for their freshness and did not pay attention to

them. It was his suppertime, and he wanted them to go
out. The women waited, but as usual did not mention a
thing to him. But of course they were old ladies, so their
mouths ran like water. They told each other of their small
grandchildren, who would be happy for whatever Satumen would give them to take home. Tea and sugar and
whatever else delicious the white men possess. The one
said that her daughter had asked for candy too. "The red
kind, the red kind," she shouted. And they told each
other that the grandchildren were as cute as grandchildren could be.

Satumen stood before them. "What are you waiting
for?" They did not understand him.

"Why not get out? Why not go home?"

The interpreter came in and explained that they just
sat and waited for his gift to show thanks for the clothes
they brought him. He became furious and told them to
go to hell.

"Us no know him," said old Samik, and out they were
dragged. Satumen had no sense of humor that day.

At home the old women explained that they had to dis-
appoint the children, but the white man wanted to be a
friend not a customer. Therefore he honored them by not
paying, but allowed them to show their pleasure by having him at the place. "And that is worth much more than
a few candies which are forgotten as soon they disappear
in the mouth, but friendship lasts while we are alive. It
never ceases."

Fall came, and Satumen learned some of the serious-
ness of the arctic. He saw the natives around anxious to
please him. Even a criminal born to fight the law is bound
to react to kindness. He also saw that in helping the na-

tives he helped himself. His scheme was now a quite new one. He would procure the greatest number of goods, then depend on some whaler calling in, and go home with him. He knew the value of furs, and he realized he could become rich. He would hide half of the fur away, so his boss, Ross Bingley, wouldn't see it if he came first. Then he would have more next year, or even earlier, if some whaler visited.

Therefore he started trading. The natives look upon a trader as a benefactor. They thank him for goods which are needed to make life easy and happy for them. The old fellows could not help thinking of the days of old every time they bought a box of matches. In their childhood it was a very difficult thing to start a fire. If they had the right kind of wood, and dry wood too, it was all right, but often they had to go to sleep without warm food because it was impossible to make a fire. What an improvement now!

But one day a young boy came complaining. He had delivered two fine blue foxes and only got a little jack-knife for them. He thought he was entitled to two jack-knives or two big knives or even more.

The old men told him that Satu, as they called him, was a man with great love for the things Bingley had left in his care. Therefore he appreciated them so much that he did not want to part with them unless he was paid high prices. Then the young man understood. He realized that Satu liked his stuff, all right. Still in the bottom of his soul he wondered that such a white man did not know that two foxes were worth more than a jackknife. And if he did not, it certainly was a disgrace and a blame for him.

Aninak came to see him, and he felt her soft skin against his face. He was a poor soul left alone in this place, where he had no power of will or discipline to stay. He felt the lack of somebody to tell him what to do. He realized that the arctic is monotony beyond description. Never had he thought of the necessity of occupying himself before. Life used to furnish enough excitement for him! In fact he used to be chased by the police and other people; now he had to chase the animals to get food for himself, and it was not what he thought the right kind of life was. But with Aninak came something soft into his life. She visited him often with her play sisters, and their chat taught him the language more than anything else. A feeling from past days, when he had innocently played with other children at home, came to him. They had a way of laughing everything into unimportance, so the hardship of the country got easier.

Satu became a fairly good dog driver. Often in the beginning he whipped them terribly, mostly when he was alone. He understood that Eskimos love their faithful animals and take care of them. But he could not help it, he had to be cruel to somebody. After his experience with Orsulik he felt ashamed. His dogs therefore had to take all his anger, and he let them have it a couple of times. But just the same, when it came to pull him home at night, when he lost the traces, they worked as before.

When he came out in the morning to harness them up, they jumped with joy, feeling his presence. The dogs got to him, made him forget his natural cruelty, and soon Satu became a lover of dogs, a man interested in his team like everybody at the place.

But others had their families, he had nobody. Everybody was nice to him, but they would have been so to any-one who came. Maybe Aninak was different, and he took her along for a ride down to a place where a little shack was put up for the hunters watching seals at the openings in the ice. She did not protest against his taking her along. She was used to doing things for him. But as they went down there, she told him that the man supposed to marry her would come for her in a very few days. Satu heard this and he felt something hurt his pride. She sat there, the loveliest girl he had so far seen in the north.

"But don't you feel sorry to miss me?" he asked her.

"Oh no, you always have been good to me and my father, but Inuiteq is a big hunter. He killed bears sev-eral years ago. In his house I will have lots to do, skins to prepare and food to cook and clothes to sew. I will be envied by other women, and I will be the one to call at visitors, 'Come in and eat, the hunter in this house hap-pens to get something to put in the mouth.' That is what women like."

Satu got sore and stopped talking for a while. She noticed it and came over to him. "Are you sorry to see someone go to another place?" she asked. Nowhere in the world are girls indifferent to attention. He said no, and took his gun and went out. He stood at the open water, where the current ran fast, so ice never covered the water. Seals came here to get an easy breath, and in the cold win-ter they are so fat that they do not sink when shot. A bul-let in the head will kill them instantly, and Satu got two before it became so dark that he could not see more.

Aninak had a fire going, and they cooked some liver and blubber together—something good for a hungry man. But his appetite was gone. She told him that he ought to have shot birds in time, when the water was freezing. Those birds could be kept frozen in the caches, good for a white man during the winter. She told him about somebody who had several ducks and geese in a cache put up for the big feasts, when visitors came to trade later on.

The fun was gone, and Satu decided to go home, even if they had meant to stay out for the night. On the sledge they did not talk, and when they arrived at the place, the girl went straight to her home and he didn't do a thing to keep her back.

A few days after, Samik saw Satu coming home with a big bag filled with something. Satu took it right in his house in the room where he kept his private things. And soon after they saw him sitting eating ducks, and when they visited him, and he was lonesome and sick for company, he invited them to sit down and eat with him. The white men have wonderful ways of cooking and everybody liked Satu's meals. Talilanguaq was a man that liked to entertain. That was why he had collected those birds for winter guests. But when he came out to his cache, he saw they were all gone.

No doubt Satu was the man that took them. Talilanguaq entered Satu's house while there was a duck meal with some girls, and chatted and joked with them.

"How we like to see a smile on everybody's face," remarked Talilanguaq. "And I feel full of pleasure seeing you took my birds."

"What do you mean, took your birds? Do you think I steal?" demanded Satu.

"Oh no, we do not use steal as a word for this," said the friendly Talilanguaq. "I am so pleased to see your behavior. You are the big man in the settlement and you have the power in hand. And still you are that modest, that you don't even like to mention your desire for bird. Can anybody show more delicacy but just go and take what he want without saying a word, just to be decent? Satu, we all like you up here, we understand your splendid ways and mind, but don't be shy, we are only silly Eskimos. When you want a thing, tell us, and it is yours. But I thank you for your lesson in modesty." Talilanguaq had talked, and the people called his speech wise. Satu asked them to join his meal, and they thanked him earnestly and were honored.

Days went and they were dark. The arctic winter was over them. It was learned that a new trader, a competitor of Satu, had come up in summertime and settled in the next fjord and had built a little house there. "But he seems not to have as fine stuff to sell us as you. Anyway he doesn't value his goods or himself, so how can we be expected to do it? Napsaq went there to trade, and he came with one single fox. But he was given an ax and files and knives and three pieces of wood for the poor little fox. How can a man be happy for his possessions when he can get them for so little? We will stick to you, because it takes many foxes to get your things. That is the way to feel proud of procuring goods, it shows you are a hunter of ability. If everyone can get everything, where is then the pleasure of work?"

Satu said that they were wise, and he promised to make his goods even more expensive. So they thanked him and were pleased.

But the darkness brought Inuiteq to the place. He brought twenty blue foxes, he had waited until he had one for each finger and toe. Twenty would buy Aninak whatever she would like from the store. Needles and shears, mirrors and white linen that would give her body a sheen and make every man covetous of her. Soap that would make her smell like the summer and tempt the hunters all around. Inuiteq would make himself talked about for his wife's sake, just as he was for his many catches.

He arrived in a party, and his twenty foxes were delivered the same night. Satu looked at him and looked at the foxes and put them away. "Let us trade tomorrow and let us eat tonight," he said.

Could anything be nicer, had hospitality of this kind been shown before? Inuiteq thanked Satu for his kindness toward his girl. "She has told about the delight in the bygone days, and she is very unhappy when she has to be contented with a miserable native like me," he added.

But next morning there were only seventeen foxes in the bag that had been kept in Satu's house. They counted together and other people stood around. Three were gone, and Satu didn't know where. But he told a story about hearing somebody coming in during the night when he was asleep. He had imagined it was Inuiteq that wanted to take back some of his skins. But evidently it must have been a thief.

"He came in through the back door and went out the same way." But Talilanguaq went out and looked and saw that the back door had not been open, the snow was lying up against it like the day before and since the last snowdrift. Satumen was mistaken. But he got mad and he asked if they wanted to trade and told those not involved to move out. Only the hunter and some of his party were allowed to stay there. And Satu pleased them by keeping his prices high. Aninak certainly got the idea, which she was very pleased to notice, that what she got for her wedding was expensive and had cost her husband some work.

She also wanted a pail and a pot to melt ice in. They were kept up in the attic and Orsulik, the faithful servant of Satu, ran upstairs to get them. These were the great days, when people came to trade. He was then a privileged man, going round and handling all the precious things as if they belonged to him. He went upstairs and looked for the pots.

"Come up and take a look," he yelled down, "we have them white and with blue rims on, we also have them gray. What do you want?"

Satu did not pay attention, he was occupied by showing goods to the hunter. A shout came down from upstairs, a cry of joy. Aninak had located the three missing fox skins hidden in a pail with the cover placed on top. She grabbed them and hurried down to the others. "Here they are, here they are. How nice that we found them. See, Satu, I can help you right to the end."

Satu scowled, but nothing could be done. He had to pay for them too, and the trading party went home discussing their things and the events of the day.

"How strange," said old man Qilerneq, when he was told the story of the foxes. "This man can keep several thoughts in his brain at the time, he is a marvelous man, and lots could be learned from him if we only had his ability."

A long time after, they told of how Satu's brain was worth at least two other men's. Like when he came home and told about having caught a seal, and it was found out that he had taken it from a hunter's cache. The traces were unmistakable. But he had invented a story himself. He was not a man—like them—who had to tell the tales from old times to get entertainment and different ideas. Satu was a man who could make a place keep awake and not stay dull during the monotony of the winter.

Once there was a terrible noise and a screaming and roaring. It was a fight of men and the people got scared and ran to find out what happened. It was Satu. He came with his man Orsulik and he went straight for the house of Inuiteq.

They were asleep in the house, and Satu said that he came to rob him of his wife. It was the old game; men want women, and they fight for them and kill each other. So Satu struck Inuiteq on his mouth and knocked him out. He ordered Aninak to get up and dress. She shivered with fear and cold, but she dressed and obeyed. Inuiteq came to, but he did not move to resist. Can a native do anything against a white man, especially one of the fame and greatness of Satu?

The bigger the man, the more need of a wife. The poor hunter does not have so many skins to prepare, and Inuiteq realized this. He surrendered from the beginning. But why hit him? He only felt pleased that the white man came to his house. There will be women for me too, and if Aninak is the choice of the mightiest man in the country, why should I complain, having had her for my delight for many nights?

So he offered to feed the dogs of the traveler and wanted to bring food and give some clothes for the girl on her way.

But Satu had no nerve to stay. He had his sledge outside, ready to leave; he had expected resistance, and it was only after real meditation he had undertaken the trip. Now it went on fine, and he had no need for his gun or use for his man.

Satu came home with his wife. But his mood was not too spirited. A criminal without a law to break is lost in this world. What can he do? There is no excitement, no stimulus for his temper.

He turned to hunting and found some interest in this. But at night when he couldn't sleep he missed something that no wife could give him. He thought of the guys he used to know, from whom he seemed to be away for hundreds of years almost. When he realized that only eight months were gone since they blew up the safe in the bank and robbed it, he wondered if this could be the same world. His friends were probably planning new jobs— ones that would make news in the papers. But maybe the damned cops would be alert and send them to jail. He himself would be up for ten years at least, that was a fact. He listened to Aninak, the ever-helpful wife he had taken into his house. He even thought of the annoyance it would be for him, when he would leave her next summer. She had been faithful and helped him a lot. After her joining his house, he was regarded as one of the tribe, and the trader on the other side of the fjord was said to be no good. How he got along nobody cared. Satu told them not to visit him, but they kept away from him voluntarily. He was no man to take after. He had no stories, no skill. When he said something it was clear like the sunshine. With Satu it was otherwise. Every time he spoke, there was a chance it was original, an effect of his brain. The other man had no such activity.

Satu got all the trade of the district, and he kept his things priced high.

The spring came and the sun returned. Ice became full of seals basking in the sun, too lazy to dive down when the natives crawled after them. A big catch assured them of caches for the winter, and their meat would be rotten and smell marvelous for the foxes, so they would be easy to get in the traps. All this good luck was no doubt due to Satu's presence.

He had shown himself a delight to the people. Had he not made himself one of them by taking a wife of the tribe, and taken her by force from the strongest man in spite of the fact that there were several women to be had without trouble—widows and elderly women who possibly were better as sewers and skin dressers? Oh no, he wanted to show himself as a man not running away from danger.

And Satu hunted seals too. He needed the exercise, and he acted like he was staying here forever. Why make Aninak sorry and let her feel she was losing him?

But he had his cache with fox skins hidden. Not a man in the place knew about it, not a single person had seen him bringing them down there one by one. There was an old ruin from the ancient Eskimos at the place. A sort of room was left there and he had fixed it so the rain could not come in. He went down there every night and brought two of his best skins. He was a smart guy. If a whaler came first, he could take all of the fur and go home. But if Ross Bingley arrived ahead of the others, Satu would have his share.

It was the *Lark* that was announced from the hill where the natives spot ships. Bingley was somewhat nervous about things. It was a new, inexperienced man at the job, but what could he have done last year? He certainly was pleased by how everything had gone. He did not resent finding Satumen married, that kept the fellow up in the country, and his stock was not bad. He invited the couple on board the ship and gave them a dinner.

How good it tasted to get a real cooked meal after a year! He saw old friends and greeted them with joy. What he had had against them last year was forgotten. He saw clearly that people were kind and he remembered only pleasant things from the winter. He told stories and people listened to him, and he felt the hero of the day.

Ross Bingley told him he was pleased. Some years of course had given more returns, but some had given less. And with a competitor across the fjord it was pretty good for his first year. He presented Satumen and his wife with several gifts: a music box, and books with pictures, and many precious things Aninak had never seen before.

The furs were taken on board, and the ship almost unloaded. Aninak wanted to show herself as the hostess at a party for the white men, and as the dance went on she became more and more happy. What a treat for an Eskimo girl; she felt her own importance!

Bingley praised her for her help to her husband, and said he himself was pleased and hoped for the same amount for the years to come. But the girl only laughed. The proud wife of a man is allowed to brag for him.

"Satu him modest. Satu modest." That was what she said. "You don't know yet, you don't know yet. Big surprise, Satu big surprise!"

The husband became uneasy: "What do you mean? What are you talking about?" Nobody knew his intentions, but just the same, a fellow always feels unsafe, and he got sore and angry. Everybody in the little party looked at him. His wife was happy over the sensation she started.

"What do you mean? Tell me what the surprise is," the boss said, but Satumen did not understand.

Eskimo humor is strange and they keep their jokes to the last, but what woman has the strength of a man? Aninak was a woman, and therefore weak. She did not have the nerves to wait longer. Her happiness was too great and complete. "Satu has a big pile of fur in the old ruined house, just outside the village. He wanted to surprise you after you think all on board."

This was certainly some sensation, and Ross Bingley was startled. "What do you mean? What is the big idea?" He looked at Satumen, inquiring by his eyes more than by words. But Satumen was an old crook and did not surrender easily. His world had been a constant fight against being found out, so he mastered the situation.

"Mr. Bingley, she should not have told you now. I have twice as many skins as you saw. But the idea was to take them on board at the last moment to surprise you, as she said. But now come and see! I want you to understand that I am better than I told you last year. Come and look!"

What a surprise! Satu had done better than anyone ever did. Better than the two other stations together, and Ross Bingley highly appreciated his man. Skin after skin went on board, and Satumen certainly got his reward. He smiled and looked happy.

But in the nighttime, when he was home alone, he took his wife on his lap and kissed her and kissed her. "I am staying up here and I will never go home." She was delighted and happy, but never had she suspected him of leaving this country, where the sun shines the whole summer, and visitors come from everywhere in the winter, where the people are gay and life is full of joy.

And in the fall they became three, and Satumen was in heaven.

Sometimes he showed her newspapers with pictures of men behind iron bars, kept in small rooms, and evidently without power to go out when they wanted to.

They were shown working, breaking stones out of a big mountain, with chains around their legs. She did not understand why this interested him so much, but white men are as they are. He grabbed his little son and kissed him.

"You shall stay up here all your life and become a big hunter, and neither of us two shall ever have any fear of coming to the big house I showed to your mother!"

III.

WHITE MEN OF THE FROZEN NORTH: EUROPE

I.

"It's Hard To Get Away"

OVER IN DENMARK we have an institution for boys who have been taken by the police in their youth. We don't believe they are born criminals. When I was a boy my father gave me a boat with sails. I could go sailing with my friends or I could go hunting in the woods and let my spirit of adventure take me out in the open. Boys who are born in the middle of a big city, especially in Europe, where no fresh air ever comes and no sun strikes the backyards where they are compelled to play, have their desire for excitement too, but the objects of their hunting instincts prove to be cigar automats or cigarettes fished through transoms in store windows or apples swiped from the dealers. For this they are taken by the police and, in order not to put them in jail and list them in the criminal records, they are put in a reform school.

In this place they may make their choice as to what trade they want to learn. Several boats take the boys out for sailing during the summer semester, and in winter they are kept in a sailor's school in the reformatory.

I usually had four of these boys with me when I went north in the summer. Up in the whaling grounds, when the killing was on, you could see their eyes light up. Here they got the fulfillment of that craving for the unusual which they had had only in dreams.

Once I had a second mate with me, a young man who was absolutetly first class in fulfilling his duties, very intelligent and always right up to his best. However, I hated that man because he was always right. Sitting in the mess when we were discussing things, he would always correct us—he always had the best information—in short, he was an unpleasant fellow to have on a ship. He was very strict with the four boys, torturing them with his mania for washing, and forcing them to behave in sailor style, and on several occasions I overheard him using the term "natural-born criminal." I told him not to do that, but as a captain it was impossible to protect the crew against the second mate.

Finally he made it too hot for the boys. It was against the rule to complain, and they were very obedient about that, but they decided to run away. They got hold of a map, showing that Greenland was not so very far from Labrador—they just had to keep going in the same direction, then they would hit the coast and, following that south, they would come down to the land of freedom. Besides, they did not intend to go back to the school next winter. While we were down in South Greenland they saved food and put it away in one of the boats. They also collected what they could in the way of clothes and the like, and one night, when two of them were on anchor watch, they lowered a boat and, followed by the other two boys, started off.

Now came their first mistake. They didn't know anything about compass variation. The variation here is very great—or maybe their knowledge of geography was not so great—anyway, they mistook east for west and went the wrong way. After having pulled the heavy boat for many hours, they found themselves at the head of the fjord. This was a big disappointment to them. One of them was inclined to give up, but the others decided to keep on and make up for their mistake by going the right way this time.

Finally, after a scanty meal, they started out again and went west. Unfortunately, they got into a thick fog and kept rowing round for a long time and finally, when the mist cleared, they saw they were right back at the ship. This was terrible for them and two of the boys wanted to surrender, but since they had not been seen, the other two persuaded them to keep on and fight their way to sea.

Again, after rowing a long time, they found themselves stranded on one of the furthermost islands. The sea was pretty rough here and in their attempt to go on shore the boat was somewhat battered. Now three of them admitted defeat. The fourth—his name was Ingolf— wouldn't give up, but told them that the thing they had to do was to wait for calm weather, try to repair the boat, and go on again.

Meanwhile, the ship had been held up for four days. They couldn't leave without the boys and, talking with the authorities in the colony on shore and sending out Eskimos in kayaks to hunt for them, they finally found them on the island, in pretty bad condition. They were brought on board, and the policeman on shore, seconded by the second mate, demanded severe punishment. I told them to shut up. This was, I understood, just a proof of the boys' willingness to take fate in their own hands, and

I fixed it so no harm was done to them. The loss of the boat was covered by falsifying a little in the log and charging it against the ship.

On the way home, the boys were working well and their natural good humor seemed restored. They sang their school songs very nicely, but every time they seemed to feel fine, the second mate would remind them of what was awaiting them at the reformatory when they would reach home and their behavior was reported.

On the way home we witnessed an accident caused by the foolishness of an owner trying to turn his sailboat into a little yacht. The occupants fell into the water and before we got a boat out to rescue them Ingolf threw himself into the water and rescued a young man by holding him up. Of course they would all have been saved just the same, but this incident showed the spirit of Ingolf, and the owner, who was an engineer and a wealthy man, offered him a position in his business.

This was arranged, and I lost sight of him for about eight or ten years. Later on I happened to meet him again. He had worked himself up and was engaged to a girl, the daughter of one of his employer's friends. Life promised to be smooth and pleasant, but one day when he came to visit his fiancée the housemaid opened the door and told him that she was sorry but the young lady wasn't at home. He asked where she was.

"I don't know."

"Well, I'll go in and wait until she comes back."

"No, I don't think so. I've been told not to let anybody come in."

The next day he received the same reception, and the day following. Finally he received a letter from the girl's

father, informing him that they had heard from somebody
that he had at one time been punished for stealing and,
though escaping jail, had been sent to the reformatory.
They did not want, the dignified father wrote him, a
criminal in their family. Ingolf had many times thought
of telling his story to the girl, but he never had because
of his fear of her prejudice, inherited from her religious
parents.

This almost broke his heart, and he gave up his fight.
He left his job and I met him down at the harbor in the
company of some very dubious characters.

I got hold of the boy and took him out to sea. I had to
be very patient with him, but finally his old spirit and
confidence were restored, and, after a couple of years, he
came back and took a course for a month. Then he met a
plain girl around the harbor. She wasn't a whore, but not
exactly the highest-class girl either. She worked as a
waitress in a cheap sailors' restaurant where the girls have
to stand for a little of everything. In her memory still
lived the old home on a little island. With his savings
Ingolf and his girl settled down on the little island, where
he now lives as a pilot in the bay. Fully realizing the mistake he made in trying to go too far in society, here under
modest conditions, with his wife and children, he tries to
find contentment in the thought that he has got everything which he could hope for in life.

THE LAPPS

I.

The Laplanders

LAPLAND STRETCHES from the Norwegian coast to the White Sea. It reaches through Norway, Sweden, Finland, and Russia. For the Lapps do not have a home of their own. They borrow what belongs to others, and even so they get the worst of a bad bargain. They end up with the deeply grooved valleys and glaciers, the worn-down Scandinavian land mass which others do not want, and the swamps infested with mosquitoes and disease. More than half of Lapland is within the Arctic Circle and the climate is frigid.

In the northern parts unbroken daylight in summer and darkness in winter last from two to three months each. Full preparation for winter must be completed by October, for November sees winter set in at its worst.

Though there is little opportunity for farming afforded by a land with this sort of year, scientists have found it to be rich in minerals. Its copper and iron, magnetite and hematite resources, are among the richest in the world. There is also an almost unlimited supply of timber, especially spruce and birch. And during the summer there is an abundance of perch, trout, pike, and other fish in the streams and lakes.

In addition to this wealth which is worked rather than owned by the Lapps, many Lapps keep great herds of reindeer, the total number being estimated at about half a million. From these animals, the skins, meat, and horns form important articles of trade.

Why would an industrious people content themselves with the moderate living that can be obtained by these means?

The Lapps are Mongolian by origin, and have been driven farther and farther north by successive migrations of Goths and Slavs. This is not only evident to the scientist from their facial and cranial formations, but also— especially to me—from their traditions, their music, and their poetry. All these cherish the memory of a happier and sunnier clime.

Are they, then, a defeated and a destroyed people, a group from which history has exacted the utmost price, disintegration? I can hardly think so from my own experiences with the Lapps. They have a happy life hunting and fishing, one which I am inclined to envy. And if they do not work as many months in the year as we do, so much the worse for us. An American, Thoreau, said that only fools work more than six weeks a year, and it must be that the Lapps agree with him.

They have never exhibited the cohesion necessary for an industrial society, nor the need for it. They prefer the wide-open spaces. And the Lapps like this, not for the sake of luxury, but for feeding their reindeer on lichens and mosses, far away from the towns and cities.

Does this make them any worse off than we are? History shows that they never fought in any war but one—that of Gustavus Adolphus. Whether this be due to their failure to develop iron or out of a love of peace I do not know. But the record is there, and it is an enviable one.

I have always admired the Lapps and loved them. There is much that can be said about their noble traditions, their suffering in history, and the pride with which they have borne the indignities which Swedes and Russians have not hesitated to heap upon them, even in the name of God.

2.

The Arctic's Strangest Story

MANY STRANGE STORIES have been told of the terrors
of the polar regions. Things were not always so bad, but
time and again arctic pioneers have faced disaster alone,
with nothing to help them but their own private resources. At such desperate moments no moral considera-
tions could prevent the mere struggle for survival from
breaking all normal restraints. Terrible things did happen at times, experiences which seem savage and unbe-
lievable when told about afterward. People who have
never known starvation are quick to pass judgment, but
in the final analysis who has the right to criticize the
actions of men who had no other chance of keeping alive?

I was in Lapland some years ago, traveling deep into
the primeval forests of northern Finland where the Lapps
have made their home along the shores of the polar sea.
This strange, mysterious people has been in flight for centuries and is even today being forced farther and farther
north by the farmers of Norway, Finland, and Sweden
who are breaking new land far beyond the Arctic Circle.
They are good people and good friends, these dark, silent
men who are marked by loneliness and poverty. For days
on end no words are spoken on the desolate farms. The

Lapps carry on their work without talk, without thoughts or dreams.

It was in such a place of cold, remote silence that I met Guolna.

He was a weaver—a strange and silent man with deep, thoughtful eyes. It seemed to me he found relief for something he did not understand in weaving the pattern of his scarves. He had only one leg. The other had been amputated for tuberculosis of the bone.

I was told that Guolna had contracted the dread disease while he was in a reformatory where he had spent ten years of his life. Why? I put the question to the local schoolteacher. Why had Guolna been sent to prison? He seemed such a quiet, kind-hearted, helpful man. The teacher could only confirm it, but did not know the reason. Guolna had been to the reform school, had been taught to weave, and lost one leg. Then he was released and had made his meager living from his trade.

I bought all the scarves Guolna had on hand, but I could not make him talk. I asked him discreetly and I asked him directly why it was that he had been sent to the reform school, but his only answer was, "I don't remember."

At last I met an old county sheriff. He told me the story from his own memory, since he had known the persons involved and had played his own part in the case.

And this is the story of Guolna:

His mother's death did not change things much, it seemed to Guolna. She had never worked much the last few years. Guolna couldn't remember the last time she had carried wood into the house, and often she had gone to bed in the middle of the day. All the other women had a job at the sawmill, but not his mother. When Guolna's father was drunk and didn't bring them any food, they starved until he was sober again.

His mother was always so gentle and good. Guolna's father could never make himself beat her, not even when he was drunk. Guolna cried a great deal at the funeral when he listened to the minister praise her as a very good woman. It surprised the boy, for he knew that their hut was the poorest and the dirtiest in the whole village. It was only because his mother had been too sick, of course, and unable to work in the house or the garden. And she would never hide their meager food, supplied when his father and friends got their pay and found courage in the bottle. They would come roaring into the kitchen and rob it of all that could be eaten. Guolna's mother would only smile and later on cry a little, wipe her eyes and smile again. And now she was dead.

Guolna and his father became even closer once they were alone.

The villages are few and far between in Finland and people are poor so far up in the north. If some of the farmers have a little money, it is only because they never give out a penny if they can avoid it. The laborers have nothing to lose. Guolna's father made a little money working in the potato fields in the fall. During part of the summer, he could make a pretty penny at the sawmill. But during the winter he refused to work for money.

There were foxes and other game in the woods, only waiting to be killed. Why should he slave for others, take orders, and work around the clock? They said, of course, that all the animals in the forests belonged to the great czar, but he lived far, far away. Besides, he was a Russian and had no right to Finnish soil. A few Russian game-keepers would turn up now and then, but they were friendly and they did not care too much for the czar themselves. A Russian is always easy to get along with so long as his boss is not around.

You could have a wonderful time hunting and even make a lot of money. But the money didn't help much during the year after he had to go to the city to sell the furs, and the storekeeper had liquor for sale. He kept an inn where Heikola, Guolna's father, turned up every spring with his furs. This was the great day of the year. The storekeeper would walk up to Heikola's table, bowing and scraping, offering a drink on the house. In return, Heikola would give the man a beautiful fox.

"That's for your girl friend, if you have any," he would say. "If not, you can always give it to your wife!"

Heikola laughed at his own joke and the spectators would roar. One is apt to applaud a man with a bagful of furs on his back. And Heikola was known as the greatest hunter in Finland.

When bargaining began, Heikola only planned to sell a couple of furs. He would be smart, only offer a few at a time, then go to the next storekeeper and sell a few more, trying to get better prices there. But every year it was the same; somehow he never got further than the first inn.

It Happened Every Year

Since he never had any money, the furs would have to pay for the grandest meal the inn could serve and the best wine and liquor in the storekeeper's cellar. As the evening wore on, every guest in the inn became Heikola's friend and drank with him. For every new bottle they emptied, Heikola would bring up a few furs as payment until at last there was not another fox left in his bag. When they reached that stage, Heikola was drunk and weeping by himself in a corner. He was thrown out in the snow, and the cold cleared his head a little. He looked for his bag and found it next to him, with all the furs gone. His friends from the inn were lying around him in the snow—but the furs were in the storehouse. Every year it was the same. Heikola went to the inn on purpose to prove to himself that he could resist temptation—and he always ended up in the snow.

After the usual futile struggle to get back some of the furs came the humiliating return to his wife and Guolna. When he came home he stayed in bed two days and two nights. At last the coughing of his sick wife woke him up and she gave him some hot porridge. She had even saved some coffee for this occasion. She never complained; she only told him how wonderful it was to have him back from the woods again. She had been scared and lonely all winter long while he was away. The good woman always smiled and told Guolna that his father was the best man in the world and the most famous fox hunter in Finland.

Guolna often thought that, after all, they only knew a small part of the country and that there might be someone equally good somewhere else. In any case, he wished that his father, with all his fame and ability, would bring home a little more food. But he knew that his father had been a soldier far, far away in the world and nobody dared to speak badly about him. Only when he was very drunk did anyone have the courage to abuse him or beat him up.

Now that his mother was dead, Heikola told Guolna that every word the minister had said was true. She had been the best woman in the world and she was the only one who had ever understood that Heikola was not a man to live so far north in the world. But what can you do when you are only a Finn—and a Lapp at that?

Heikola told his son not to feel badly any more. Guolna was a big boy now. He could come along to the big forests this winter and go hunting with his father. There was nobody else in the woods. There you could dream in the dark nights. The fire would make strange figures and shapes, and give you thoughts you could not understand yourself. That was why he always longed to go back to the forests. When he came down again from the woods, he was sick from his dreams and crazy from loneliness. He would want to forget it all and start drinking to try and be a great man, if only for a few hours. When he ran out of furs, the shameful ending came with Heikola beaten up in the snow. But up in the forest there was no beating, only the hunting with your life at stake. There were the northern lights which cut their way right into your soul.

This year Guolna should come, and all through the winter Heikola could talk with him so he would not have to drink when they came down to the village again. Once they had money, they would make their way to the city and look at the big houses and buy all sorts of clothes, listen to music all day long, and get their hair cut by a man in white clothes. Just you wait, little Guolna, you'll see what it's like, coming home again in spring.

Heikola had to spend his last penny as payment to the minister for the beautiful words he had spoken over the grave of Guolna's mother. When they finally left, his equipment was even worse than before, but this time the boy was along. He would teach the boy the tricks of fox hunting. They would have a wonderful time together.

It was a long, long way to the wild forests. Guolna was sometimes so tired at night that he could not fall asleep. His father would make an open fire and they ate what they had been able to catch in the woods. Heikola made traps and caught grouse, so they had plenty of meat. It was only the pain in his feet which kept Guolna awake at night. He would lie staring at his father's face, thinking that the expression looked different from anything he had ever seen there before. Sometimes his father would look like a bear or a wolf. Then again he might look like a bird or a lemming. The flaming fire threw its weird shadows and made a stranger of his father.

Heikola had to carry Guolna across the rivers and through swamps and sometimes Guolna's short legs could not keep pace. That was nothing to worry about, Heikola said. They wouldn't say anything about it when they saw other boys. "We'll share many secrets which nobody will know or understand. You don't have to be ashamed if I have to carry you once in a while."

Guolna didn't know how far they had gone when Heikola finally said that they had reached their goal. The wind was too strong on the barren mountain, he said. But by the edge of the woods he knew of many caves and old huts where they could settle down comfortably for the winter.

A Secret Shared

They made themselves at home and waited.

At first Guolna did not know just what they were waiting for, but his father told him that the Lapps would be taking their herds of reindeer this way just before the snow became too deep. The reindeer would be hungry. They couldn't be kept in a flock. Heikola knew how to attract them. He would gather heavy bunches of moss which he flung up in the trees close by. The animals would smell the moss from far away and come running for it. Then Heikola would go into action. He carried a long knife which he would plunge deeply into their throats as they stretched their necks for the moss. The reindeer would give plenty of meat—some of it for eating, some for trapping foxes. This was the great secret which nobody but Guolna knew—for he was a big boy now, and his mother was dead, and Heikola had nobody else to share his secrets with.

They sat by the fire together, making traps for the foxes. They had to make very sharp wooden stakes to keep the meat in place in the fox traps. Guolna learned how the traps had to be set up and how to erase all his tracks when he left the traps in the snow. The fox was the smartest animal in the world, his father told him. Heikola showed him how to skin a fox and soon Guolna felt he knew all there was to know. It seemed quite senseless for him ever to go to school again with a teacher who only made the boys and girls sleepy.

Heikola told his son many other strange things—like how he had been born on the other side of the border, on the Swedish side. In Sweden there were policemen who wanted to put Heikola in a big dark house because he hadn't wanted to be a soldier. A soldier was the worst thing in the world. He was forced to wear boots every day —so hard that they made holes in your toes and heels and ruined your feet so you could never go hiking in the mountains again, even with the softest of *komager.*

A Father's Dreams

Heikola had been a prisoner but he had escaped and now he could never go across the border again. When he was a young man, he had lived in the mountains with the reindeer keepers. It had been a wonderful life with plenty of food and more money than they could count. But misfortune had struck his family and his life had been one of poverty ever since.

"But I'll teach you how to become a great man, with plenty to eat and with heavy clothing of the thickest wool, Guolna my boy. You shall never have to wear leather pants, and your shirts will be white and washed just as soon as they get dirty. There is nothing in the world I won't do for you. You are the one who is always in my dreams when I am alone."

That night Guolna stayed awake for a long time. He thought that his father was a very great man, for he was fighting with other people to get reindeer for his traps. Guolna had heard a lot about reindeer thieves, but it had never struck him before that the thieves were in constant danger and had to be very, very clever to carry on, year after year.

His father made skis for them as soon as the snow came. As long as the weather was clear they could not look for reindeer. The men they were waiting for had stolen the reindeer themselves, and could only cross the border during a snowfall heavy enough to cover all tracks. They were dangerous people, the reindeer thieves. They knew they were hunted. They were desperate in defending themselves, and quite merciless.

One evening Guolna asked his father about the war. He would like to know if he had shot many enemies and what kind of people they were.

"I have never been in the war," said Heikola. "That was only something I told people to make them afraid of me. But I have been a soldier and there were many of us who had been in the war. They were admired and respected. When I ran off, I had to keep away from people until I crossed the Swedish border. Since then I have always had to be careful not to cross over to the wrong side of the border again. But I have been living up here during the winter and I have trapped many a reindeer which the Swedes would otherwise have stolen from Finland."

The following night Guolna didn't sleep much either. He saw his father in an entirely new light. He thought that he was a greater and more wonderful man than before. He was fighting single-handedly against a whole people. He had to use his own head—that meant much more than going to war where you only did what the general said, and shot the people you were told to shoot.

One day winter arrived with a tremendous gale. It had been snowing once in a while before, but now the wind was screaming and the snow whipped right through them. Heikola told Guolna to curl up in the little hut and promised him that they would soon have the softest fur for a cover instead of their miserable leather pieces. Soon they would be stuffing themselves with juicy meat and go to bed sucking marrowbones. This was the right kind of weather for chasing a herd of reindeer across the border, and Heikola would be out there, too.

Guolna begged his father to be taken along, but he was told that he had to wait until the first few herds had gone by. Then Heikola would teach his son how to fool man and beast. The men had to be made scared of mountain ghosts, the police, and the rightful owners. At the same time you had to make the animals believe they were being chased back to their own herd again. That was why you had to be alone and not have a partner to ruin your chances.

Thus Heikola set out—and that was the last Guolna saw of his father alive.

Once he was alone, Guolna soon fell into bed and let the screaming storm lull him to sleep, dreaming of meat and tallow soup and furs to sleep in without ever feeling cold any more. He had no way of telling how long he had slept when he finally woke up, but since Heikola was not back yet, he just turned around and fell asleep again.

Soon hunger woke him and he discovered that the hut was full of snow. The fine flakes had fallen through the holes in the roof and the cracks of the door. Now they covered Guolna and everything in the hut. Guolna didn't let it get him down. He saw that the storm was over, so he swept out the snow as best he could. He thought it strange that his father wasn't back yet. He had probably caught so many reindeer that it would take him quite a while to skin them all and hide the meat. It was better that way than if he had come home as soon as the wind had died down.

Guolna couldn't sleep any more. He just sat there in the hut, looking forward to all the meat they were going to eat. He made up his mind that he would eat the tallow first and while the meat was boiling he would suck out the fat marrow of which he could never get enough.

Soon it was night again, and still no trace of his father. Guolna had seen a touch of daylight in the horizon to the south so he knew it had been day. He didn't want to cry, though—his father would notice it at once, and Guolna didn't want him to think that he had been scared.

Guolna's Search

The following day Guolna didn't think he could live through another night. He didn't know what was going to happen. Wolves might come and there was no protection against mountain ghosts when he was alone. One had to be two to be able to look both ways at the same time. Ghosts vanished when one looked at them, crossed oneself, and said the Lord's prayer.

Somehow he managed to live through the night and at last he could glimpse a faint shimmer of light again. Finally, he decided that he had better go out to meet his father. Heikola must have such an awful lot of meat to carry that he would certainly need some help. Guolna remembered how his father always helped him in every way; now it was his turn to help his father.

He walked on and on until he reached the foot of the mountain, but there was nobody to be seen. Guolna realized that his father must have lured the reindeer into the woods and killed them there. That would have been the wise thing to do since he could not be seen among the thick trees while he skinned the animals.

But when he came down to the woods again, there was no sight of Heikola. He must have gone to the little hut then, and they had missed each other. Guolna had the true Lapp's instincts for finding his way, but when he was back at the hut again nobody had been there. He was tired now, and very hungry. He was glad, though, that he was more tired than hungry since he didn't want to eat until his father returned. He felt sure he would be wakened by his father standing in the door with a heavy load of fresh meat which he would throw to the floor. Then his father would laugh and say he was sorry he was so late.

It was a miserable little Guolna who woke up finally. He had had nothing at all to eat for three days. He couldn't think any more, he only wandered around in a daze looking for his father. He realized by now that Heikola had been unlucky. The thieves must have discovered him and that was the reason why he had to hide in the woods now. But let the thieves catch sight of Guolna, then they would be scared and run away. Boy, oh boy, how Guolna and his father would laugh! And then they would eat.

In the evening he felt no hunger any more. He was only sleepy and very cold, but he managed to walk back to the hut to make sure that his father wasn't there all by himself, eating all the good meat.

The moon was out and showed him his way when he left once more. He knew that his father would do anything in the world to help him. He also knew that he would freeze to death and starve without his father. He had to find Heikola. Maybe his father had met some friends who had offered him liquor. He might be drunk, might have fallen asleep some place. Guolna had to find him and wake him up. You can sleep on and on until you die if you settle down in the snow with your mouth uncovered in the open air.

When he reached the spot where he knew that his father had gathered a heap of moss, a fox suddenly ran past the boy. Without thinking, without even feeling miserable because of his loneliness, he followed the track of the fox. This was how he found his father.

Heikola had been dead for a long time. He was partly covered by snow. He was completely stiff and frozen all over. But the worst thing was that the foxes had nibbled away quite a bit of him.

At first Guolna couldn't think, couldn't even stand up. His legs were like soft wool stockings. He had to sit down in the snow for a long time. Later on he began to cry. The crying didn't mean anything, he didn't feel like crying. The tears just came by themselves. After a long while he suddenly remembered that now he was all alone here in the bare mountains. There was no possibility of getting down to people again at this time of the year.

Alone in the Forest

He didn't quite know why he went back to the hut. He had nothing to do there, nobody to help him. But he had covered the long way back to the hut before he realized how foolish he was. What should he do? He wondered for a long while, then cried when he got tired of thinking. Every time he realized how helpless he was, he could only think that he had to talk to his father about it. It was wonderful to have such a wise father. But he wasn't there any more! And Guolna had to cry again.

In the morning it was clear to him that he simply had to find food. You must eat, he told himself aloud. But he had to laugh right away for there was not a thing to eat in the hut or anywhere else. There was no use crying, he scolded himself.

He had seen the fox by his father's body. A fox could be eaten. He had to go after it. It was a good thing that his father had taught him how to set the traps. When he came back to the hut he would show his father what a good hunter he had become.

Stupid thoughts! He had to pull himself together now! He trudged all the way up to the corpse of his father and he could see at once that more foxes had been nibbling at him. They had dug a little tunnel through the snow down to the body. Where the snow was firm, just where they hurried in and out of the tunnel, Guolna set his trap. Then he erased his own tracks as he left, as his father had told him to do.

Thus he got his first fox. With his knife Guolna skinned the animal on the spot. Back in the hut he cooked the meat and it tasted like a dream of all the best things in the world.

Guolna felt like a different person when he had finished his meal. He made himself a more comfortable bed with pine branches and the fox fur and then he slept for a long time. When he woke up, he finished the fox and then he sat down to consider his future.

Guolna told himself that there had never been anything in the world his father would not have done for him. There was no reason for him to ask for permission to set up the fox traps by his father's body. The dead man would help his son now, as he had done when he was alive. Guolna felt quite happy at the thought as he retraced his steps and set up two more traps by his father's body. In the evening he got another fox. It was large and fat, fortunately, and it kept Guolna going the next two days, when it was snowing so hard he could not go outside at all.

By the time it had cleared again, he had had an opportunity to consider his situation. He realized by now that he was utterly alone. He cried a little as he made his plans, but not as much as he had expected. He was too busy with the work of keeping himself alive. And now he set himself another great task. He would bring his father down to the village again in spring and have him buried by the minister. He should rest right next to Guolna's mother, under the beautiful cross which Heikola had made, and carved with her name, her dates of birth and death.

He had to get food to keep alive. Food meant foxes and there was no shadow of doubt left in Guolna's mind—he knew his father would agree to let him use his flesh to bait the traps.

It was dreadful to cut up his father's flesh, his dead body, but it was so dark he couldn't see, and had no chance of feeling ashamed. Besides, he had no choice.

Soon it became routine. Every time there was a fox in the trap, or when a fox had gotten away with the bait, his father's body would have to yield flesh. But he was glad to give—Guolna knew his father better than anybody had ever known him. Other people had not understood what a great man he was, how he had always been victorious. Now he had finally met bad luck. A knife had killed him. Guolna had seen the wounds and knew there had been a hard fight.

Every time Guolna went up to his father, the body grew smaller. He had to serve his son as bait. There was nothing else for Guolna to do. If he were to die himself, he would never be able to bury his father in consecrated ground, and Heikola would become a ghost of the mountains. Guolna had to keep on living and he could only do it with his father's help. The great Heikola, the good and strong Heikola, who was his father. But . . . but there he was! As he trudged heavily along on his skis from his hut to his father's body, he kept thinking of the funeral he would give Heikola. Afterward the two of them would go away together and spend all the money they got from the furs . . .

Oh, dear God! Heikola was not his father any more! He was only a dead man who would never come back.

Guolna skinned the foxes very carefully, dried the furs, and soon had a whole bag full of them. The sun was beginning to appear by then, a little bit more of it every day. Foxes were getting rarer and the grouse were coming back. One day he noticed a drop of water in the sunlight and he knew it was no use going after the foxes any more —they wouldn't go in the trap.

By this time, the head was all that was left of his father, but Guolna was used to it by now. He didn't mind any more that his father was getting smaller and smaller. He even thought it was typical of his wise father not to run out until he was not needed any more.

The Journey Home

At long last Guolna could begin the trek back to the village. The snow was melting and he had a hard time moving on his skis. He walked day after day, and when he was able to catch an occasional grouse, he ate it raw because he didn't want to make a fire. Once in a while he was close to people, once he heard a dog barking and saw sleigh tracks in the snow. He didn't know why he was reluctant to meet anyone. Perhaps he was afraid they would take the fox furs away from him. Perhaps they would ask about his father and then he was sure he would have to cry. He did not want to cry.

Soon he couldn't use his skis any more. He left them behind and continued on foot with his two bags over his shoulder. In the one he had all the fox furs, in the other the head of his father to be buried next to his mother. The head would have to be placed in a coffin, and over the grave the minister should tell about Heikola's great life, how he had been a soldier and shot the enemy. All the world would understand that one of the heroes of Finland was being buried.

It took him a long time getting home this way. He didn't want to go by the shortest route where he risked meeting people. The minister should be the first man he would speak to.

At last he came to his home village. His plans had been made very carefully. He would not take the fox furs along to the minister, who would only think that they were meant for him. The furs had to be sold to get money enough for the long trip that Heikola and Guolna planned to . . . No, there came his crazy thoughts again!

When he came close to the minister's house he could see that it was Sunday. There were lots of people outside, but all the men were inside as usual. The minister would give them a schnapps to keep warm on the return trip, maybe a cup of coffee even. Guolna hesitated a moment before he decided that this was a good opportunity to let everybody know that Heikola would never be seen again. Guolna felt as if his father only died at this moment when he knocked on the door and stood in the minister's house.

He felt sorry now that he had not stayed in the woods with his father. Nonsense, he told himself. He couldn't have done that. He had to bury him in consecrated ground. But Guolna could no longer remember what he planned to say to the minister. He stood rooted to the floor without saying a word.

"Hello," said the minister and gave him his hand. Guolna noticed how dirty and ragged he was now that he stood next to the minister.

"You are Guolna, aren't you?" asked the minister. "Heikola's son?"

Guolna didn't answer. Of course, the minister knew him since he had spoken such beautiful words over his mother's grave. Now he was going to find other words in the Bible to say over his father's grave.

They stood there for a long time staring at each other, the minister and the boy. But at long last it had to end.

"What do you want? Do you have a message for me?" asked the minister.

"Yes," said Guolna. At last he could speak, for the minister had said the right thing, had mentioned just what Guolna was there for.

"It's this way, you see," he told the minister. "I have just come down from the mountains because I want to make a funeral for my father."

"Your father? But is he dead?"

All of a sudden Guolna wanted to cry again. He was scared and he felt that all the thoughts he had had in the mountains were unimportant, they counted for nothing now when he faced the minister, who was such a learned man. Guolna was terrified when he saw all the books on the shelves. The judgment was pronounced in those books, all men were sentenced there. That was why he lost his voice suddenly. He could not say a word.

"When did Heikola die?" somebody asked. But everything was in a haze now. "Where have you put him? Shall we bring him down from the mountains? Did you bring him along?"

Oh, dear! All the questions they fired at him. Couldn't they stop? This was not the way he had planned it. Guolna wanted to leave them again. But where should he go? Now he could see how wrong it had all been. He should not have brought his father down. One of the farmers should have gone up there with a wooden coffin, then he could have been carried down and Guolna could have sat on top of the coffin. But there was nothing left to put in it—only the head!

At last he thought the questions came closer. But he had to shout to make them hear him. "I have him right here," he cried at the top of his voice.

"The boy is impudent," scolded the minister. "He

shouts when he should be quiet. Perhaps there is not a word of truth in his story. Heikola was a most unreliable person. His son is surely like the father."

Everything went black in front of Guolna. He took his bag from his shoulder and opened it. He let his father's head roll out on the floor. The next thing he knew, they were all screaming.

He fainted, and nobody wanted to touch the boy who had eaten his father's body in the mountains and now brought the head down for a funeral.

When the screaming subdued and the minister had asked the Lord for strength to endure this terrible thing, the women were let in. They had heard all the noise and didn't want to miss anything. They all talked and explained, remembering old and terrible tales.

At last one of them said they had to do something with the boy, even if they did not want to touch him.

"What wickedness and sin I am witnessing in my congregation!" complained the minister who had recovered sufficiently at last to say a few pious words.

Guolna was beginning to come to again. He wanted to get up but somebody kept him down. He was not to be allowed to stand up again and run away. They had sent for the sheriff. They would keep him down until he arrived and took Guolna along to prison. Yes, they would all keep him down.

Guolna's Scarves

Yes, I bought all Guolna's scarves. I wanted to bring them along to Greenland and let the Eskimo girls enjoy their strange figures and patterns. I knew they would make me a popular man with the Eskimos.

Alas, they never got to Greenland. On my way home I had to go to Stockholm where three young ladies caught sight of my scarves. Two of the scarves could be turned into the loveliest blouse.

I got back to Denmark at last, but the girls at home were even worse. There was nothing I could do once they had seen my scarves. A blouse made from Guolna's scarves was seen on the stage of the Royal Theater in Copenhagen. The costume was praised in the newspapers.

"What an artist that weaver must be!" they said to me. "And what an incredible sense of humor he must have!"

I managed to save two of the scarves and brought them with me to Greenland. I believe the stewardess on the local steamer is still wearing them.

3.

Sons of Isak

LIFE MAYBE IS TOO SHORT, time goes too slowly, yet spring is always behindhand. The snow always takes too long in its thawing. And why? It's not good for skiing any more! In its thawing all it does is flood the brooks and the lakes, make swamps of the valleys. One must wait and wait before the country is fit for traveling again, and the grass dry enough to lie down on, the berries ripe.

However, so long as the snow covers the grounds, at least one has peace from the mosquitoes.

Isak, thinking such thoughts, walked along ahead of his herd of reindeer, climbing the last mountain. They were not far from the pass by the glacier and then Isak would look down on Norway. Soon after that he would smell the salt sea air. Suddenly he remembered happy days, the reindeer browsing on the green slopes, folk doing nothing but strolling about in the birch and pine woods, picking berries through the nights when the sun never left, when the midnight sky glowed with both sunset and sunrise at once. Then it was wonderful to be alive.

Isak's thoughts were not clear. He did not go on with them, for the dogs had failed him again. Down there his reindeer were headed for the woods. They had espe-

cially dainty tastes in springtime; his cows, round with
calf as they were, especially liked the lichens on the trunks
of trees, and were not above taking the bark too. That
was all right. That was understandable, but sure as rain
the farmer who owned those trees would come and he
would claim his whole wood had been ruined. Then the
Lapp had always to pay. Everybody knew that. The Lapp
was wrong. The Lapp paid. You had to be careful these
days keeping your herds in a territory that seemed to get
narrower and narrower, or you'd have trouble with the
superintendent from the Swedish government. He'd likely
pop up any time, anywhere, making a big noise. In the
time of Isak's father the Lapp had this whole country
to himself. That was a wonderful time. But now there
were boundaries, Finnish and Swedish and Norwegian
boundaries to be respected, invisible though they were,
and how could reindeer be expected to see the difference
between Finnish lichens and Swedish—or even Norwegian?

They climbed upward and upward, but slowly. The
herd was heavy and slow. Today at last they would cross
over into Norway. The *raid* was way behind hand this
year. Sara had lagged, too, though usually she could keep
up with any of them. Finally she'd let them go on ahead.

Isak knew nearly every stone and torrent and tree
along this way. Soon now they'd be going down and the
grass would be green and fine. The Swedish side gave
shelter against the west wind, but on the Norwegian side
the snow melted faster, grass and herbs were up earlier.
Oh yes, Norway was a good country for a Lapp when
spring at last had gone by.

They found a level place, sheltered, for camp, and the
deer slowly scattered, feeding. Now the men could sleep.

They slept for hours, woke to eat a little, to look over the herd sleepily, to sleep again. Now the cows would be dropping their calves, and they'd not move on for at least two weeks, for the calves have soft hooves which must harden before they can follow along over the stony trail.

The women, far behind this year, caught up. Isak saw the first of them down the mountainside. Perhaps they had news—no doubt about it, they had news—but Isak was not impatient. He did not wonder what it might be. A Lapp is not likely to wonder. When the time comes one will learn what there is to learn. That was that.

The woman who had climbed up ahead of the others paused by a great rock to shout that Sara had given birth to a boy. Great news for Isak!

He took his lasso and hung it on his shoulder, called his dog and went out to count his reindeer. He said to himself, "Sara is a mother. Well, then I am a father. I have a son."

The cows had found protection behind bushes and rocks here and there, each in its own place. Some stood motionless. Others walked away a little. The newborn calves lay on the ground, heads feebly up, nostrils quivering, and some were uncertainly on their legs, too long and too thin. Isak went quietly, cautiously among his herd, for he knew that if anyone touched a newborn calf these first days the mother would never take to it.

Sara, he said to himself, had turned out to be what she seemed—a good wife, clever with the reindeer, good at sewing, and in the tent. She was a good wife, and her first was a son! There'd be more, Isak said to himself. He felt good, and could not stop walking over the mountain even after he had counted all his herd. When he returned to his *kote* in the evening it was filled with people. They were drinking hot coffee with plenty of salt, so—as they said—it would taste like something.

Sara was there, the little one at her breast. Isak looked across at her and he thought that she was good to look at. The baby surprised him. He had seen plenty of newborns, and they were all ugly, every one of them, but this one—his—was for some reason quite different. One even liked to look at him. During the night he decided that the boy was to be named after his great-grandfather who had been prominent amongst his people. Petula was his name. Petula—that would be the name of Isak's eldest then.

When the calves could keep up they broke camp and went on into Norway. Sara had made a *komse* for the little Petula so she could carry him on her shoulders as she walked, or put him down on the ground if she worked; but if they had to leave him where wolves or dogs could be expected she simply hung the *komse* on a branch of a tree.

Petula was christened in the church of Kvesmenes. There was a big christening party, Isak butchering a huge reindeer, every bit of which was boiled and eaten. After that, stewed fruit and then—best of all—coffee with ether drops. It burned the throat and warmed the heart. They all got wonderfully drunk. Let the Norwegians and the Swedes brag of their akavit—coffee with ether drops contained fire and power, and you could buy it in most any store. As the brew went around the noise grew and became a roar, echoing up the mountain. Isak, being the happiest there, shouted the loudest. He was a father. His herd prospered. Sara was his wife.

For all that he did not take too much. Let those whose ownings were unimportant, or nothing at all, be care-free, let them get drunk and laugh and yell. He, Isak, had too much to take care of. He must remember his duty, even at a christening party, so he got up and left them and walked over the ridge to a lake where his herd was pasturing. He took them by surprise. They raised their heads, fearful, ready to run, but then got his smell and recognized it. He went quietly among them seeking a calf, a fine one, the best of all. He saw two that might have done, but let them go. He had in his mind another he'd glimpsed the day before, finally found its mother. Her skin was smooth and glossy; she was big and strong. He threw his rope and caught her around the horns.

At that, outraged, she leaped to her feet and set off downhill, dragging Isak helter-skelter after her. He was strong, however. He knew more tricks than she did. Soon he had her standing, could stroke her all over. He found no faults. She was the best of the lot. Her calf, he was sure, would be like her, so he set out for the camp, and she, unwilling, doubtful, nevertheless followed. The calf came trotting and kept close to her mother's flank. But the calf hated the smells that came from the different *kotes,* especially the smoke of the fires, and when they came too near she turned back.

"She'll come along," Isak said to himself. "She still needs her mother—just like Petula," and he went on. When the calf came up again Isak stopped to let her get some milk, and even while she suckled he dropped his lasso around her neck. Then he let the cow go, gave her flank a great slap to persuade her on her way, and the calf, fighting, shaking with fear, was dragged down to the party. The smells outraged her nose, the cries of the dogs frightened her. To make it worse men came and stroked her sides.

Isak called to Sara to come out. "And bring the boy," he said. "Let him see his reindeer."

Petula only cried, even while they took his hand and with it stroked the calf's head. That was all right. Later on he wouldn't cry about that calf!

Isak took his knife from its sheath on his belt and cut into the edge of the calf's ear, marking her with a special mark for Petula. He spat tobacco juice into the wound so that it would not grow together.

Sara smiled. Her son—he was not only her son. Now he was a man of property. Isak would take care of this calf, but her mark would always show that she was Petula's, and when she had calves, they would have Petula's mark, and their calves would, so if God was good and if Petula was a lucky one, this single calf would be many when the time came for Petula to be a bridegroom himself and have his own *kote*.

They let the calf go. Sore-hoofed, her ear burning, she never stopped running till she had found her mother again.

II

With fall the snow line crept every day closer down into the valley and the Lapps turned back toward Sweden. Life is travel. Back and forth. They met the winter high in the mountains. It was a terrible winter. Well, that's what heaven willed. So be it. Spring would come again. Little Petula was carried a year in the *kamse;* then he was driven in a *pulk* with his half-grown cousin. Then he was up—not so quick at this as a calf by a good deal—and walking on his own legs. And then he was big, managing the reindeer with his father Isak.

He was by then no longer Isak and Sara's only one. There was Nila, next Aslak, finally Heikola; four sons for Isak, and all four so well taken care of by Sara, who sewed their clothes, their shoes, looked after them in every way, while Isak taught them what they should know. And as with Petula each of the other three at his christening party was given the best calf Isak could find, and it was branded so that it and all its progeny could be forever the property of that son.

The summer he was twenty-one, Petula, the oldest, the lucky one, apple of his father's eye, went walking through the trees with Inga. He came back to his father and said now he would marry and set up for himself.

Isak and his four sons rounded up the herd and went among them seeking out Petula's earmark.

In twenty-one years Petula's calf, that beauty, had become three hundred and five reindeer, many of them unusually big and strong.

"You were born to good luck," Isak said. "Look for yourself. These are all yours, my son. Now it is for you to take them."

Shortly after their wedding Petula said good-by to his parents and to his three brothers. He looked with expressionless face at their father's depleted herd, and he and Inga set forth, crossing the mountain with some young people of their own age, friends from childhood.

Among them, Petula, having by far the most reindeer, and being very capable anyway, became a leader.

Nila, the next brother, was the odd one, and of course also the unlucky one. The other brothers, Aslak and Heikola—one married but stayed with his father, the other married and went off. Neither of these was lucky. They were not terribly unlucky, either. They were in between and for the moment there's little to be said of interest about them. But that Nila—from the very beginning he was different from Petula.

Nila was a specialist in being interested in the wrong things, in trouble, in discontent—in being unlucky altogether.

Not that he was useless. Even as a boy he was a great hunter. He hunted wolves, tracked bears to their hibernation. It seemed that reindeer were not enough for Nila. He liked to get away from the herd and the family. He would be absent for days on end, and when he returned he never spoke a word of where he had been or what he had been doing. He seemed to be running away, like some sort of solitary animal. All the same, one day he turned up outside the *kote* with a girl nobody had ever seen before. She was dressed in Finnish style. Nila's parents stared at her. Isak's face did not change, but Sara, behind him, had to hide hers. Even then you could hear her laughing, for to them the Finnish clothing on the girl seemed odd and comical.

"Who is that?" Isak asked Nila, staring at her.

"She is the woman I want to be my wife."

Sara did not laugh any more. She and Isak looked at Nila in astonishment. Why did he not come to them for advice before making such a decision?

Isak said, "She is handsome, but what use is that when difficulties come?"

"Who is her father?" Isak asked. "Has he many reindeer?"

"She is an orphan," Nila said. "She used to live in the government house."

Isak shook his head slowly. "You have bad luck, my son," Isak said. "So it comes to this." And he pondered. "The day you were christened, and with all your brothers," Isak said, "I gave you a calf, the best I could find. That first year it was stolen. A stolen calf does not increase, my son. You have no property of your own. Go then, and become a reindeer thief and do as well as you can, for what else is there for you?"

Nila did not answer his father. His face showed no resentment, or any other feeling. He would not have been a Lapp had it been otherwise. Nevertheless, as he turned away with his strange girl, he was looking at a fact. Petula, his brother, was rich, but he himself had been chosen by fate to be a thief. Well, that was the way of the Lapp. Could he argue with the word of his father?

Still he was not quite without property, for at their wedding Petula, camped a long distance away though he was, heard of it and sent a man with a team of sledge reindeer for a present.

Afterward Nila and his wife went their way, and at the first station they came to, Nila sold the two animals for ether. He drank well and wildly for days. After that he and his new wife disappeared into Finland. A policeman came and asked among the Lapps for Nila, saying he had emigrated without asking permission, and not only that. There were a number of properties belonging to

farmers near the village that had disappeared. The policeman was given such answers as the Lapps chose, but he
wrote them down in a black notebook all the same.

III

Aslak was the son after Nila. Aslak's calf was eaten
by wolves early in its first winter. Aslak married Rebecca
and after trying to earn a living making things for nosy
fools called tourists, they returned to Isak's *kote* to live,
and there Aslak was willing and even glad of the chance
to work as a herd boy for his father. The calf of Heikola,
youngest of the four sons, lost its mother before it was
full-grown. It never caught up: its offspring were often
weak, many died young, and while others grew big they
were never of the best. When they had calves of their
own they could not scrape away deep winter snow to
reach a real sufficiency of the moss underneath. Heikola's
herd numbered twenty-eight. When he married, he drove
it away and mingled it with a friend's, but he and his wife
had the mark of poverty on them, and it was to be always
so with them.

The herd of Isak still grew. He was a great man. Swedes
and Norwegians came often to his *kote* for a meal, and
sometimes slept the night. The government superintendent himself invited Isak to come eat with him when
Isak drove his herd to Karesuando. Isak, who had hoped
well of life, had seen his hopes gratified.

Sara was old. She could still keep up, but one fall
when Isak came in to say that now it was time to break
camp and head back toward Sweden, she only got started
doing the many things she must do before she sat down

again and then lay down in her place, and said she was tired. Two days later she was dead. Isak did not weep. His expression did not change, for he was a Lapp. He looked at her and said if she had to die, then how much better it was for her to die here instead of in mid-journey when she might have held up everything.

But later he tasted lonesomeness.

They were high on the mountain. He went out and looked at the low sun, knew black winter was coming swiftly upon them. Perhaps this might be the last sun for him, too. Well, he felt no regret for that. That would be according to the way it was. And he had been a happy man. Four sons, and he—and God—had given to each of them his destiny. He, Isak, had dealt full and equal justice among them the day they had been given to God—therefore what happened afterward was God's wisdom. Isak thought this through, looking back at the steppes of Norway; then he returned to the *kote* and went to sleep at once. Next day he told Aslak and his other herdsmen to change their route to the east. "We are going to new grounds," he said.

Unquestioning as always Aslak ran out ahead on his skis to show the herd the new way, the others rounding them up. They went on then, slowed by the deep snow. Just before noon they came upon the tracks of a large herd, a rich man's herd. Their hooves had beaten a broad road. Here and there on either side where the drifts were not deep, patches of ground had been rooted in.

They kept on until the animals were tired, made camp and rested briefly, getting off next morning under the stars. That afternoon their animals knew the other herd was not far off. They and the dogs and the folk on skis pressed on faster. They came upon them on a wide smooth slope, and at once Isak's herd dashed in amongst that other herd. Herdsmen shouted, furiously angry, and dogs came yelling. It would be a devil of a job to sort the animals out, one herd from the other. Some of the strange herdsmen came back, at their head the rich Lapp himself, but they could not keep up with him for it was Petula, Isak's eldest—and Petula had always been faster than any one else on skis. On skis he did not run, he flew, he soared like an eagle.

Now he came in with a great spurt of powdery snow all about him as he turned and stopped. He began at once shouting, but Isak turned to him. Petula saw it was his father, that it was his father's famous herd which had mixed with his own.

Isak said, not smiling, hardly opening his eyes, "No use to take the trouble to separate them, my son. Soon they will know each other, soon it will be one herd. Yours."

IV

Thus Isak and his people joined with Petula, and thereafter Isak lived in Petula's *kote,* cared for by Petula's wife, Inga. She was a busy woman who knew how to manage, though folk found it hard to be friendly with her. She was too commanding, and too careful of what was theirs. Doubtless, though, it is thus that those who have kept what they have. Isak's son Aslak understood how things were at once and he saw to it that he kept busy. He hopped around like two men, was always with the herd, serving it and its owner, Petula. At night while all others, even the herdsmen, slept soundly, Aslak slept with one eye open as the saying is. When the dogs raised up the desolate and alarming howl that meant they'd scented wolf, Aslak was the first man out; and each morning he was the first man at work. He was a treasure; and for all he did, Petula, his brother, who was rich, gave him his food—his and Rebecca's. That was all.

And Petula prospered now as no other in Lapland. He lost very few animals, thanks to Aslak; his herd grew in numbers, in health, too. When they butchered in the fall, Petula took enormous quantities of meat to the store; and when he brought skins to the dealer, it was like mountains moved down the mountains on his many sledges.

Isak who had never known he was tired of leadership found it cheerful and comfortable to follow. He just strolled along with Petula's throng. When Inga handed him his food—to him she always gave plenty, and more than plenty, you may be sure—he was thankful. Those two, his son and his daughter-in-law, were known far and wide and respected everywhere, for they were rich, and to be respected one must be rich, no doubt about it! Well, Isak's own industrious life had laid the foundation for all this. That was a deep satisfaction. Isak looked at the vast herd that was Petula's—at the *kotes,* all the herdsmen, and sledges, the many dogs—and Isak understood why on that day when he had felt lonely for Sara, God had advised him to give his herd to Petula. Just look: if he had given to each of his sons a fourth, as he might well have, not one of them would then have been really wealthy.

Aslak kept the wolves away, keeping at it like a man who could never be tired, and he killed more wolverines than any Lapp before him. That was service indeed to Petula, for the little wolverine is the Lapp's worst enemy, far worse than the craven wolf. The wolverine is stronger than any creature of his size: he does not know weariness nor satiety. He is always ravenously hungry for reindeer meat. His jaws are like steel traps, they can crack thigh bones. And his cunning might make a fox seem a fool!

Aslak was so clever, so fleet on his skis, he could track a wolverine down and, if he were in deep snow, run so much faster that he would run in swift circles around him, tormenting him until, with unerring aim, he put a bullet through the wolverine's head. Then he would bring the skin to Petula, and Petula would say kind words to him. Inga would pour him out an extra cup of coffee, putting plenty of salt in so that it might taste like something. Aslak was pleased too, but lying beside him at night, whispering lest the others in the *kote* overhear, Rebecca, his wife, not so submissive, not so easily satisfied, said he should have had the skin himself to sell to the dealer, and so have a bit of money. Aslak said no, but she kept at him about this, sure that right was on her side. "Do you get any wages?" she would ask Aslak, and then herself give the answer, "No." "Don't your wife and children, just like other wives and children, need this and that which must be paid for with money?" And she would answer herself again, "Yes, they do, Aslak."

She convinced the man at last. When next he brought in a wolverine's pelt he spoke to Petula, repeating Rebecca's argument.

Petula heard him through. Inga was there, too, and they both sat silent for a long time. Isak came in, lit his long pipe, sat down. Impassive as they, Aslak waited. At last Petula having arranged the words exactly right in his head spoke. "Are the reindeer yours?" he asked.

"No," Aslak said.

"Are the wolverines then the enemies of your reindeer?"

Aslak pondered this. "No," he said at last.

"If the wolverines are the enemies of my reindeer," Petula said, "they are my enemies, and so their pelts are mine."

For the life of him Aslak could see no flaw in this reasoning. He sat silent. Isak, their father, spoke after a long silence. "Your words are clear and right, Petula," he said.

Rebecca whispered at night: "Did you ask him?"

"I did," said Aslak.

"And did you have any luck?"

Aslak did not answer. Silence was an answer. She understood. One does not chatter in Lapland.

When the winter had gone and the sun came back to them it was at first colder, as always. This was the worst time. Gales roared through the mountains. Snow piled into bottomless drifts. A bad time for skiing; also it was the time the herd demanded most care—the time not only of wolverines and wolves, but also that other predatory animal, man, the reindeer thief.

Isak was old. He broad face had more wrinkles than a herring has bones. But his legs seemed young as ever. He went out with Petula, a northwest gale with a voice like a man's yowling in their ears. They ran around the herd, checking it over.

A man on skis makes very little noise even in calm

weather and in all the noise of a gale he moves in what is as good as utter silence. So Aslak had swooped down and was between them, shouting before they had any idea of his approach. "Thieves," he shouted. "They've killed three and are off with the carcasses on a sledge. The runner tracks are down there! They haven't been drifted over yet, so they've not got much start on us."

Aslak leading, they started in pursuit: Isak, Petula, and half a dozen herdsmen who had followed Aslak. They found the trail and ran toward the valley, following it, swift as angry eagles, the lot of them. Soon, miles away, on the floor of the valley, spotted over with clumps of pine, black from here, they saw the horse-drawn sledge, no bigger than a fly, and a moment later in full charge, so to speak, going like the wind, leaping ledges, and even in steeper slides, skimming over the tops of pines, they closed in and were seen. There were two men in the sledge, beside the carcass, and seeing their pursuers they must have known it was all up with them, but they made a last try. Then abandoned the sledge, took to their skis. The horse stopped the moment the whip ceased. It was covered with foam, exhausted.

"Drive the horse and sledge back," Petula told one of his men. "Take them to the *landfiscal*."

And then on after the thieves. Aslak was already out of sight. After him a single file of young men, then the older men with Isak and Petula. Petula could have led, but his dignity demanded that he stay with the older men.

The thieves had been surrounded. They had given up.

To steal reindeer is the worst crime of all. Alas, it is also the most common crime in Lapland. There were the two thieves. Here their righteous pursuers, but among the latter everyone had at one time or another caught a roaming reindeer and kept it, but now was their opportunity to sit in judgment. It was a pleasure. They felt, everyone of them, virtuous and superior.

But Aslak only gazed at the taller of the captives. It was his own brother, Nila.

When Petula came up he said, "So it is here, in such a situation, one at last meets one's brother face to face."

Nila smiled. He took his mitten off to shake hands.

He had said not a word to Aslak but to Petula he spoke freely. "My big brother!" Nila said. "He does not smile then at finding that he has parted with a bit of meat for his unimportant relative? Truth is, Petula, I did not know it was yours, but I shot only because I was hungry, and worse than that, my wife and the boys are hungry, too."

Isak looked surprised. "You have sons? I did not know that."

"You did not ask me," Nila said. "If you had invited me to visit you I could have told you that I had sons. We often hear of you," he went on, as talkative as some outlander, "but we never hear that you have said we would be welcome in your *kote*."

Isak was silent. Indeed, uncomfortable as the circumstances was, he was pleased to see his son. But Petula was angry, and growing tall with outraged dignity.

"Listen, you," he said in a loud voice. "I shall turn you over to the *landfiscal*. He will put you under arrest and the judge will punish you for this."

Aslak and the others were surprised. After all, here were two brothers face to face. The second thief, a Lapp from Finland by his looks—give him up, perhaps; but the brother?

"Three only I took," Nila said to Petula, not begging favors, just speaking out. "Can't you spare that much from your great herd, brother? Remember I got not one single animal from our father."

"You should have asked me," Petula said righteously.

"Would you have said yes?"

Petula considered that, made honest answer: "No," he said. Nobody smiled. "Look at Aslak," Petula said "He owns nothing. But he does not steal my deer."

"Aslak is your servant," Nila said, coldly.

"This is too much talk," Petula shouted. Now Isak came in. "My son," he said gently to Petula, "let your brother and his strange friend go this time. Forgive him now, and let us be friendly. I am old. I will not live long. Let it be so, that all my sons may attend my funeral."

That seemed to settle matters. But Nila, seeing his horse and sledge being led away in the distance, spoke out urgently, commandingly to Petula, "Brother, make haste! Tell one of your boys to run after my sledge. Quickly. Do not go against your father's will."

Petula was not one to be commanded. His stubbornness rose up in him.

"Reindeer thieves!" he cried harshly. "They are the pest of this country. It is not as it was. Now there are boundaries, laws. Violators of the law must be taught a lesson! It is my duty to have you arrested, Nila, for you are a criminal, even if you are my brother."

Isak could say nothing. They turned around all of them and started the long run to the village and to the *land-*

fiscal. He was an astonished official to see a Lapp bring in his own brother. "But he is a thief," Petula said, "as all my men can tell you," so there was nothing to be done. Nila and his Finn were placed under arrest.

The bell in the little church was ringing as the others all came out of the *landfiscal's* house. It was Sunday and they were in time for service. They trooped in, sat in two rows, and at once went sound asleep, every one of them, making a loud comfortable noise with their breathing. That was the way of the Lapps. Enclosed by God's words and the soft slow hymn music they slept better than anywhere else, and awoke when the service was over, feeling stronger and better, full of grace.

Two weeks later Petula heard that Nila had been sent to prison, sentenced to hard labor.

v

It was torment to sit indoors, but it was worse when Nila had to go outside in the prison yard and walk around. Feet that had never known anything but soft skin shoes were tortured by the thick prison boots they gave him. But he had to walk round and round twice a day inside the walls that were so high he could not see over them.

He learned a good deal in that prison. Among other things the trade of blacksmith which he took to at once. He had always been clever with his hands, even though he was born to be unlucky, and a thief.

He was taught that he was a strayed sheep. If he did not return to righteousness he would go to hell and stay there forever. Nila bent his head, told the holy man this was all true, but inside, Nila laughed. He was all right, that holy man, but what did he know of the life of the Lapp? Reindeer thieves were as unavoidable as summer and winter. Why, Nila's own father had dedicated him to that life, recognizing his nature, which was of course given Nila by God himself. Who else? Strange this man of God did not see this.

The man of God, observing Nila's calm and humble conduct, said, "There is a man who has made up his mind to be a better man." And he recommended that his sentence be shortened.

It was in the last days of winter that Nila, a free man again, rode into Karesuando in the bus. He was changed, a well-dressed man in a black overcoat, with a red handkerchief around his neck, and so many boxes and suitcases that the driver had to give him a hand. Lapps stood around watching as always when the bus came in.

"How do you do?" Nila said. "This is me. I have returned."

They said nothing, not knowing whether to remember that he was a thief returning from punishment or a well-dressed outlander with a wealth of baggage. Nila walked past them all and into the *landfiscal*'s big house. After a while Silla, the servant, came out and said that Nila had sat at a desk, and with his own hand, with a flourish, signed his name several times. Thus Nila had not only earned a little money in jail—for the black coat, and so forth—but he had become a learned man. It was a little bewildering, but then much that came in from the outer world failed to make sense. Now there was a something called war over there in Finland and white men were burning and blowing up the houses of white men, killing their women and children. Craziness. Some Lapps recently arrived had told of long lines of refugees moving on foot and horse sledge across into Sweden, town folk, what had they to do with the fighting?

The learned and well-dressed Nila came out again and looking at no one went across the street to the house of the dealer, he who bought meat and skins.

"I want to rent a room for one week," he said, and his words were relayed at once to the wondering folk outside. "Perhaps I will stay longer, but first I want to find out if it suits me." Haughty words! Here was a man with demands about food and bed. Yes, here was a man who had learned a good deal.

Nila set up a blacksmith shop at Karesuando. He was good at all sorts of smithing but his specialty was knives. He made a wonderful knife, bigger than those you could buy in a Swedish store, well-balanced in the hand, handsome, and useful. And, next to skis, what is so valuable as a good knife?

Nila's wife and his two sons returned. They had been in Finland all this time. They were happy to get away from there. Things went so well with Nila that he could rent a little house and buy a horse and a sledge to travel around in from farm to farm, carrying his forge and his tools. He was well liked, for he could light up a dull winter's day with a funny story. Lapland in the dark time isn't the merriest spot on earth, and that's true.

Sometimes, for several days together, Nila would be gone, no one knew where, and Nila did not say. Well, perhaps he'd gone to some very distant farm to do his work. It was noticeable, of course, that Nila's house never

wanted for meat. He was generous with it, too. Nobody
ever gazed down onto his well-filled platter in Nila's
house and asked, "Well, neighbor, where did this meat
come from?" That would not have been polite.

Folk were pleased to be invited to Nila's house. There
was plenty of food, plenty of coffee with enough salt in
it to make it taste like something, sometimes ether drops.
Then they all got drunk. But when Nila was celebrating
he just laughed and was happy. He did not want to fight,
or shout at folk when he was drunk.

So it went until the folk arrived from Finland, relatives of his wife and others, two dozen of them almost,
older men and women and half-grown children, Lapps
all of them, who had lost the way of following the reindeer, but had lived in town, the men working in the
nickel mines. Now they had to leave because the Russki
were coming in, killing and burning.

Nila put them where he could. It was a job with a
house of three rooms. After that came the task of feeding
them. But news came down the river that the great herd
of his brother Petula was not far off, and Nila sent a boy
to Aslak to ask Petula for meat for the hungry Finlanders
who had descended upon him. Aslak went to Petula but
what he brought to Nila's messenger was not a promise
of meat. "No. The war has sent prices up and up for reindeer meat, so how can I afford to give it away to that jail-
bird and thief, Nila?" This was the gist of his reply as it
was brought down to Nila. Nila went out to his forge and
labored, and the blows of his hammer rang out all over
the village.

Sunday he did not go to church. There he would meet

his brothers and he did not care to. He sent his wife. She was his eyes and ears. She listened to what folk were saying. She talked to Rebecca, Aslak's wife.

"Why don't you come to us and drink a drop of coffee?"

"Maybe that could be done," Rebecca said. "First I must ask Inga, Petula's wife, if she can manage without me."

"It must be fine to have a steady job," Nila's wife said. "When one has a steady job one has money every month, in cash." She knew of course that they were not paid a bit of cash. "Now, Nila," she said, "has to rush around from one farmer to the next and like as not he is paid for all his work in goods of some sort."

Rebecca wanted to show that she had teeth, also. "Well," said she, "can't you count on a bit of cash now and then—from hunting?"

But Nila's wife was not one to take such bait. She smiled and said that Rebecca's Aslak must also come. Plenty of everything, she promised. Tomorrow the moon would be full, and with the snow as it was now, they could run down on their skis in no time.

Next night they came. While all the refugees could not be invited, some of the men were, and the others were content to remain in the other rooms. So far there'd been food for all, and they were warm, besides being far from the planes and the guns of the Russki.

Nila told his brother Aslak how happy he was to see his face again. Much snow had fallen and thawed away since last they had sat together in a *kote,* feeling relationship.

"Ah, yes," Aslak agreed. "Now our father is dead. And he was buried without you."

"There was a little hindrance kept me away," Nila said. They all knew the "hindrance" was steel bars but no one spoke of that. The food was good, and plentiful. Also Nila had given Aslak his finest knife.

With the coffee Nila brought out five small bottles of ether. Now Aslak realized how long it had been since he'd felt the fire of that wonderful drink in his mouth. He accepted his cup eagerly and soon it was empty, but Nila poured often, generously. Pooh, how it burned one's throat. Nowadays Petula could not allow Aslak to be drunk, ever. With Aslak drunk who would look after the reindeer? No, as it was, only one of the two brothers in that *kote* could drink, and that one was not Aslak.

After a while Rebecca also took some of the reeking, fortified coffee, though she did not care for the taste. She had no head, Rebecca; as soon as it burned in her mouth it flew to her brain and she began to talk. How she talked! There was much hatred hidden in her soul, more than she knew herself, and now it all came out. She remembered Inga's insults, all of them through the years, the unnecessary demands. In the first place, why had Isak given all his herd to Petula, Rebecca asked, her voice rising louder. If he had died before doing that the superintendent would have stepped in and seen that each of the sons got a fourth of the herd. Then they'd all have had something, and none would have been a slave, or worse than that, a beggar among the tourists, the stupid, hateful tourists who had cash in their pockets.

Then, one winter Aslak had carved a wooden goblet, the most beautiful thing you ever saw; it had been ordered in Norway by a tourist. But as soon as it was finished Inga had taken it! What happened to the fine soft skins Rebecca tanned? They became clothes for Inga's children. When Aslak carved knife handles Petula looked them over and kept the best of them, saying that they had been carved on his time and were therefore his, though Petula himself was incapable of carving anything. Yes, but he had money. He put it in the bank. Money had the ability in that Petula's *kote*. You put money in the bank and it called more and more money to it.

She talked on and Nila said not a word but listened all the while. Aslak was asleep. He was drunk. All at once the stream of talk stopped, as a torrent stops suddenly when November night brings a hard frost and it is frozen solid. Nila looked at his wife. She understood. They went outside. The moon had set but it was a clear, still night, the slow pale flames of the northern lights licking half the sky. They could hear the low voices of the refugees, the snores of some. They'd be hungry soon, all those homeless folk. Nila stepped on his skis, his lasso hung on his shoulder. Away he went, and his wife went back into the house.

VI

Petula's great herd had *beited* this year rather close in to the village—an hour of fast going and he'd be in sight of it. The snow, very fine and dry, was stirred by a slight wind, and that was perfect. That was God's grace, Nila was sure, for as it lightly drifted it obliterated his tracks, and yet the wind was not too strong. It did not fight him.

The frozen-over river in its broad valley was at his right as he flew along. Now on his left, far off, dogs bayed. That would not trouble Petula, comfortably sleeping on his skin bed. Petula did not know that his faithful Aslak was lying dead drunk in Nila's house. Not only that—the two other herd boys had gone too, one across into Finland, just over the first ridge there, the other farther up the river where there were other camps, and attractive girls to fool away the moony night with.

Nila took his time. He had plenty of it. As he climbed and swooped he thought of his wife, that clever woman, who had told him of all she had learned keeping her ears open at church. He thought of how she had helped him prepare everything and instead of resenting her indigent, unfortunate relatives and their friends, he felt suddenly that it was time he gave her some special present. He was near Petula's herd now, huddled in groups all across the slope of the sparsely wooded hillside, and at once he got his lasso around the neck of a fine little calf, brought it down, and thrust his long knife into it. He had the skin off it before it was cold, a fine soft skin, just right for part of a coat for his wife. But now he buried it in the snow, having first, of course, cut away the ear-marks.

Then he went on. He meant to circle the whole herd. There were close to a thousand animals in all there. It was like going to the butcher shop, not exactly exciting, but he had not come out tonight for excitement.

Hu-i. He threw his lasso around the horns of a big fellow. It jerked back, reared up on its hind legs to bring sharp hooves into deadly action. Nila slipped to one side, and with a swift, powerful stroke had his long knife up to the hilt in its neck. Lifeblood, black in the strange night light, curved out, shining, and the big one was on his knees, and died in silence. A reindeer thief must know how. He must be quick and cunning as a bullfighter. He must make no mistake. If the deer does not die at once it will flounder about. May even get away, leaving tracks and blood everywhere to tell the tale of the theft. No, one must bring him down at once, in a moment. Nila knew his business.

To skin a reindeer is no great trick. Throw him over quickly on his back, then the knife into the belly, then cut downward at the back of the legs to the hooves, around them. The skin is so loose it can be pulled from the ribs with the hands. Nila liked the heat around his fingers as he worked, the last heat that would come from that body. Then deep in the snow he buried carcass and skin. He would come back. He would not forget. A Lapp can always remember the place, making a picture in his mind of the tree over there, the boulder, and so forth. It's as simple as opening a suitcase when he comes back.

He killed five, skinned them, buried them. His movements were deliberate and slow, yet he got it done in no time because he made no mistakes. Well, that was food for all his enormous new family for a time. Nila could smile about that. He was quite a man, Nila was. Here he had a blacksmith shop, friends, and who could question his having much meat? He was often paid in kind, wasn't he? He really felt like laughing. And yet the work for that night was not done yet.

He dropped down again closer to Petula's *kote,* through the clumps of reindeer, huddled in the drifting snow, quiet, for there was a smell of wolverine in the air, and when there is danger, the reindeer, who can be wild and stubborn, turns meekly for protection to man.

With all his force Nila started yelling at the animals. At once far away the dogs raised their wild voices. Petula on his warm pile of skins stirred comfortably. Thank God for Aslak and the herd boys! They'd get out and put a stop to that, whatever it was, at once.

But the dogs continued. Inga woke up.

"Aslak! Aslak, where are you?"

Inga was already out. There were two *kotes*. In their own, nobody else but the children who slept deeply. In the other was only old Mother Hylla, who was deaf and who spent her days sewing shoes and tanning skins.

"Petula," Inga cried. "Nobody is at home. Aslak is gone, and Rebecca with him!"

So the big man, the grand one himself, must get off his bed and look after his herd. He called his dogs and set forth, disappearing at once in the stir of dry snow. Two dogs went on ahead of him, two followed.

Nila watched his approach from a hiding place behind some spruce trees. Now for Nila came the moment he had thought about in prison down south. He had made sure of meat, and by now the snow had drifted over the blood-stains. He was safe as to the meat. So he had shouted. Here came his rich brother, Petula, straight toward the trap, which was simply Nila's lasso rigged so that one side of a wide loop hung in the branches of a birch tree by a rock where Petula must pass before looking down on his herd.

As Nila waited, the barking of the dogs came a little nearer. He smiled.

VII

Petula was in a hurry. Perhaps, near as they were to town and the *landfiscal*, it actually was a thief instead of a wolf. The dogs were certainly in a fury. He outdistanced them easily on his skis as he dropped down from the crest of the second hill. It was near here the deer had *beited* yesterday. They'd not have moved far. He swore at Aslak, his brother, for having gone away. But they were all alike, these servants one had to depend upon!

Still, it was good to get out in the night, racing downhill on skis as in his younger days, with only a slight wind, and the night so clear.

Just then, having approached that tree and that boulder, passing between them, something seized him by the ankles. He fell forward. What? Petula had taken a header? He struggled in the soft snow, and sat up. There was a man there standing on his skis, looking down at him, laughing.

"Need help?" Nila asked. He had Petula's ski pole and now threw it from him.

Petula was more astonished than anything.

But a man without skis in deep snow is lost. It was not only that Petula floundered, a captive of the snow over which a moment before he had flown like a bird, but his dignity was gone. Without his skis he was in worse case than a knight without his horse. He was nobody, a laughingstock.

"It's little me," Nila was saying with a grin. "You see, I wanted to see you once more, just once more. I've been away so long from you."

"What is it?" Petula asked. "What do you want of me?"

What did he want of Petula? Nila had to laugh and he leaned back to do so, making a noise about it, so that the dogs, circling uncertainly, yelped back at him.

"You stealing reindeer again?" Petula asked. "Ah ha! I shall have you punished again!"

Nila said nothing. He coiled his lasso carefully, silently, hung it again on his shoulder, where it belonged.

Then he came nearer and dug up Petula's skis which he had lost in his floundering about. Nila stepped away a little, and took out his big knife from his sheath. Up to his waist in snow Petula watched as Nila slowly cut his fine skis into chips.

"Here," Nila said. "Here are your skis, brother. Run fast, then, back to your *kote* and get help."

"Do you mean to murder me?" Petula asked. "Listen, Nila, it is true I sent you to jail. That was my duty. It was necessary that I protect other reindeer owners against thieves."

"Our father gave me not a single animal," Nila said. "My calf was stolen. Our father told me then to go out and become a thief myself."

Petula was getting very cold after his fine fast run over the snow.

"In that jail I suffered," Nila said. "I was indoors all the time or walking round and round the yard in terrible boots that hurt my feet. I thought how you had much and I little."

"Nila, my brother, listen to me." Petula was pleading now. He was frightened. He did not want to die. "Nila, go down and get new skis for me. Do that for your brother. Then I will give you reindeer meat for you and your poor friends from Finland. That was wrong in me to refuse. I admit that. Get me new skis, for now I am helpless, and I shall remember only that we are brothers. You shall see that I can do good as well as harm, Nila."

Nila looked at the sky.

"Speak that little speech once more, brother," he said.

"It was a beautiful speech. It gave me pleasure to hear it."

"I mean it," Petula said.

Nila laughed. It was a loud, terrible laugh. It mounted up and filled the night. It sounded to Petula like the laugh of some ambassador from hell itself.

Nila, secure on his skis, stood there laughing, fingering his long knife.

"Don't kill me!" Petula said.

Nila controlled his laughing. "Petula, you forget entirely the most important part. I am a son of our father. You got the best of it. All right. But now I have made up for everything. Now I have seen the mighty Petula begging for mercy like any little man. And now the powerful Petula will have to get home as best he can on his feet. He will arrive at his *kote* tired out, but having had plenty of time for thought. So good-by, big brother. Come down and visit me."

VIII

When Nila reached his house it was already morning but still dark as night. Breakfast smells came from houses that he passed. His wife came to his door. "Well?"

"It is all right," Nila said.

They went inside. Aslak slept on his back in a corner, mouth wide, snoring like a nickel-plated horn.

"Meat?" Nila's wife asked.

"Aye," he said. "Plenty!"

And then when he had drunk some coffee he went out to his smithy and lit the forge, for he felt too good to sleep. He set to work, his hammer sending its cheerful loud cry out across the snow-covered fields.

"Here," Nila said later to Aslak, who stood holding his aching head. "Take this knife—my best one—as a present to our brother Petula. Now mind, on the way back, take the route by the river. Maybe you will come upon your brother Petula then, and he may need your help for he has lost his skis," Nila laughed. But Aslak only held his head. He wanted fresh air and he and his wife Rebecca set out at once.

Watching them go Nila thought this had been the best night of his life. He was grateful to God's grace for all He had done for them. A heavy burden had been taken from Nila's shoulders, forever.

And there was meat for all of them. Already butchered. He had only to send for it.

GREENLAND

I.

Greenland an Open Country

GREENLAND IS a Danish colony.* It has always been, as far as political questions are concerned, though logically it might have been expected to be Norwegian. The old Norsemen, Eric the Red and his son Leif Ericson and their fellows, came from Iceland, and Iceland, after some centuries of independence, was subject to the Norwegian crown in 1261.

But when at the Congress of Vienna in 1815, after the Napoleonic wars, Denmark was forced to cede Norway to the king of Sweden, her three possessions were entirely forgotten. Thus Iceland, the Faroes, and Greenland remained Danish.

For a long time all three possessions suffered a state monopoly that hindered progress. Now, for many years, the Danish government's exclusive right to trade in Iceland and the Faroes has been abandoned, and Iceland has become a country in its own right. But it was only in 1948 that Greenland was opened up. Until then the

---

* This is no longer true. In 1953, Greenland became an integral part of the Danish kingdom, represented in the Danish parliament by 2 members. —D.F.

This and the following piece were written by Peter Freuchen before, during, and immediately after World War II. I have permitted what he said to stand, but have added notes where conditions have changed.—D.F.

royal trading company had kept sole right to trade and exploit the country; at the same time it was next to impossible for foreigners—including Danes—even to visit the colony, or to take part in its activities, unless granted permission by the Danish state.

It must be admitted that conditions among the people in the three countries are not to be compared. Iceland and the Faroes are not only inhabited by Scandinavians —they are much closer to the rest of the world. Greenland has its remote situation in the arctic, its strange Eskimo inhabitants with their difficult and special language and their economy of natives exclusively occupied with hunting and a little fishing and trapping.* And there is also the immensity of the land, which stretches not less than 24 degrees of longitude, from about 60 degrees north and up, making it the closest to the North Pole of any land in the world.

Greenland is still in great part unknown and unexploited—for example, in the matter of valuable minerals, the mining of which may yet be found to present great opportunities.

Denmark has done an extraordinarily good job in taking care of the people of Greenland. This is proved by the increase in population, which has moved steadily forward, from about 6,000 in 1805 and 10,000 in 1880, to a present total of 28,000, Danes and Greenlanders included.

In our day not many of the people could be called Eskimo. Very few—only some in the extreme north and on the east coast—can be counted as pure Eskimos. The

---

* Greenland has, since this was written, generally expanded its economic life and has improved its communication with the rest of the world.—D.F.

mixture of Danish and Eskimo blood has proved to be an especially fine one. Nowhere in the world have arctic people reached such a high stage of culture and progress; in fact, the modern Greenlander does not yield to any other nation in the world so far as intelligence and education is concerned.

I, for one, was most surprised to find that an Eskimo translation was made in 1948 of *The Count of Monte Cristo*. It became the best-selling book of all time in the Greenland stores. Not less than 3,000 copies were printed and sold out in a hurry—and that in a population of only 22,000 people at that time.

Very few Danes understand Eskimo. On the other hand, there is everywhere a strong desire to learn Danish, with the result that there are now about 18 Danish teachers placed along the coast.* The American method of sending out teachers to Alaska who know nothing of the native language has been taken up—so far with splendid results. The small children of the Greenlanders are very interested in learning Danish. The bigger ones are not too good at it, but after some years everybody will be able to understand and to read Danish, and so get their share of the motherland's literature and culture. There is now a special daily radio service from the little capital, Godthaab, and on top of this many of the more prominent Greenlanders listen every day for news given in Danish. In the more thickly populated areas movies are shown frequently, though of course the expense must not be too great. But the settlements are for the most part extremely small, due to the extraordinary political and physical conditions of the past.

---

* In 1962, there were 115 Danish-educated teachers in Greenland.—D.F.

In the beginning there were only sealhunters, with their kayaks and umiaks, living in Greenland. No other way of existence was known. The main thing then was to keep the entire population scattered along the coast. This often caused bad feeling between the trading people on the one hand, and the church and schools on the other. The church was run by the Danish state, after the Moravian missionaries left in the year 1900, having baptized practically everybody. Not less than 170 different stores existed to supply the natives with essential goods, and consequently the villages stayed very small indeed.

But times have changed. The climate is turning warmer. The water is not so cold as it used to be, ice does not form so thickly as in earlier days, and the animal life is changing too. The seal which used to provide the only means of livelihood, furnishing food, fuel, and clothes, is now disappearing. Besides, there are so many new ways of making a living that sealhunting is going out. In its place fishing grows more and more important every year. Now the sealhunter is rare, though he is still looked up to as the real he-man, the original supporter of the society. But fishing brings in the cash to take care of growing developments and progress of all kinds.

Today you will find just as much variety of occupation in Greenland as in other nations of the world. People are buying their clothes. Much of their food and wood for buildings is also purchased. Iron for other purposes, tools, guns, and what else you need is to be had—when you can pay for it. Also a number of Greenlanders are now occupied in the mines—and this industry may have a future which should not be overlooked in observing the picture today.

The school system in Greenland is organized on Danish lines and is set up to be equal to that of Denmark's, except in remote regions where lack of children makes it impossible to provide many educated teachers. The state supports a teachers college, and high schools are to be found both in the northern and southern sections.

No less than four newspapers are printed in Greenland, in Eskimo.* Two of them are run by private enterprise, the two biggest are subsidized by public funds.

The people of Greenland are to some extent self-ruling. The communes elect a little council, of which there are thirty-six members in all.† This community council takes care of minor things, such as help to the poor, orphans, widows, and the aged. They also give compensation to hunters or fishermen who lose boats, guns, or other gear. The community councils are elected by common and secret vote. Only recently the women have won the right to vote like the men.

Above the community council is the municipal council, called *Sysselraad,* which looks after items pertaining to greater districts. Also these *Sysselraads* are privileged to take care of criminal situations. Crimes such as theft and sexual crimes are brought to court here, and acted upon. There are no prisons in Greenland. Sentences are mild, compared to those pronounced in the United States, for instance.

Highest of all is the *Landsraad,* which is a provincial council. There are certain rules for electing the mem-

---

* There were nearly 20 newspapers in 1962, most of them bilingual.—D.F.

† Since 1961, a council of 16 members has local jurisdiction over all of Greenland.—D.F.

bers of the *Landsraad*. These are not absolutely democratic, as up to now the state, represented by two gover-
nors, has had a big hand in the elections. This will now
be changed from year to year, to bring about a really
democratic system.*

The money for the enterprises of these councils is
taken from a fixed taxation on all goods and products
brought to the stores for sale. Twenty per cent is with-
held from the native, and out of this every public expense is taken care of according to certain rules. But in
modern times many inhabitants are not delivering goods
to the stores—only buying.†

The altered condition of things in Greenland worked
itself out during the war. Americans came up not only
to defend the country. The United States also brought in
supplies for the people who were cut off from Denmark
during the five years of the occupation, and the Greenlanders learned to know different kinds of goods. The
Sears, Roebuck catalogue became the most popular
book. By the time of the liberation, Greenland had had
a peek out into the world. This caused the prime minister of Denmark, Mr. Hans Hedtoft, to decide to put an
end to the state monopoly. He took a trip to Greenland
in 1948, with an offer to the *Landsraad* to open up the
country, so that Greenland might function under the
same conditions as any other country in the world.

The parliament of Greenland accepted with a unani-
mous vote, and on that day *the last closed country in
the world was closed no more.*

---

* The change has now been completed.—D.F.
† There never has been a direct tax in Greenland, but there are taxes on
certain products paid by the consumer indirectly.—D.F.

Greenland was open to private enterprise, and both Greenlander and Dane enjoyed the new state of affairs. Of course there were still many regulations to be put through. Everything could not be done overnight. But the decision was made—the monopoly of the state was dead. The future looked bright and prosperous for the northernmost country in the world, ruled up to then in as efficient and humanitarian a way as any colony in the world by little Denmark, whose pride Greenland certainly has been for ages.

2.

Greenland: Past, Present, and Future

WHEN THE WAR WAS OVER, the world was changed, and that didn't mean only those countries where cities had been destroyed and people killed. It meant also places far removed from the battle areas, and far removed from the world, such as Greenland. From days of old there has rested a mysterious dimness over Greenland and every-thing connected with it. This was not surprising so long as sailing vessels were the only means of penetrating the ice and reaching the shore. People went there for whales, and they saw natives who lived and dressed quite differ-ently from anything they had seen before. At that time the men on the whalers were inclined to be frightened at almost everything; they saw deadly danger everywhere.

Right up to our days an old-fashioned regime held sway in Greenland. Many of those who were employed there thought they were to be pitied and deserved more consideration than if they had remained in Denmark. Yet the fact is that the temperature in Greenland never goes as far down as it does in Wyoming or North Dakota.*

---

* Except, of course, on the icecap.—D.F.

As for the natives, they are easier to deal with than many other people. The idea that Greenland is a country of desolation will disappear in the future. Radio has already put it in touch with the outside world. Aviation has made it possible to go and come whenever one wants to.

In the old days the sailors had the further disadvantage of being told by their teachers that Greenland could not be approached except at the height of summer. It was true, of course, that the great ice pack kept out sailing vessels, but the old-time schedule was not changed even after steamers and motorboats came in. No sailings during the winter. It is only recently people have learned that winter is an especially good time, inasmuch as the ice does not blockade South Greenland. The drifts of ice from the east coast do not start till summer.

We want no more of the tales about Greenland as a region full of danger and mystery. Incidentally, the young natives who are being educated in Denmark should be told not to allow themselves to be exhibited at parties and festive occasions wearing native costumes, like a zoological garden, pretending to be a wild people, and making a show of themselves. This is all the more absurd as many of the young fellows in their homeland never wear the costumes in which they appear at these affairs.

Greenland must for the future be put on the map as just another country, and it has many means of holding its own. Many people think of Greenland as an immense region. True, it is big, but on the map generally used, the so-called Mercator's projection, on which the globe is rolled out flat, the northern and southern regions of the earth are all out of proportion. Greenland is spread out to look larger than Australia, whereas in fact it is not quite a third that size.

But Greenland is right on the spot. If we look, not at the flat map but at the globe, it will easily be seen that if anyone wishes to fly from Chicago to Moscow the route will cross Greenland. An air route from San Francisco to London will cut the northern part of inhabited Greenland. And who can doubt that future transportation will be in the air? There is no other place in the world which in the past has been so isolated and in the future will be such a land of transit as Greenland.

I am no expert in these matters, but I do understand that a number of air bases will be in use from now on. We all know that the United States government has built huge air bases somewhere in Greenland at immense cost and with immense expenditure of labor. These have been in use during the war and must be utilized also for peace travel and for mail. They will surely be kept up.* Of course the same is true of other places in the world. I only hope that the airports in Greenland will be run by Danes, and I think this is a reasonable demand on the part of any country that harbors such places.

The arctic is wonderful for flying. For several years the Russians made flights from Fairbanks, Alaska, to Soviet bases right across the North Pole. Just think of the lives lost, the terrible labor and suffering the very term North Pole conjures up in our minds. Today the pole is right on the route. To future voyagers there, Greenland will be of importance in emergency cases. The route is easy. The pilots do not need to climb to high

---

* And they have been. They are now NATO bases.—D.F.

altitudes; they have as a rule fine weather, and the darkness does not frighten anybody in our day.

Airports should be established in Greenland and supported by the Danish government. But this is not all. We must have a first-class meteorological service there. It is now known that the weather of Europe is, so to speak, made in Greenland. Its big glacier and other conditions have such a powerful influence that weather forecasts from Greenland can predict storms a day or two ahead. This is important not only for the pilots crossing Greenland by air, but also for navigation by water and for other traffic in far distant places.

Therefore Denmark must organize meteorological posts in different places on the east coast and have them run by capable scientists. This will be an expense, of course, but also a great benefit to all countries. Norway already had some stations on Jan Mayen and a minor one on the East Greenland coast, but it is for Denmark to do it right.*

What valuable minerals Greenland contains nobody really knows. We Danes are not a mining people. A little has been done to explore the possibilities, but only sporadically. It must be done systematically. If we have not the proper specialists ourselves, we must get them from other countries, from Canada or Sweden or wherever we can. But Denmark has a wonderful opportunity in possessing this great and, from a geological point of view, very interesting country; it could be used for the education of young mining engineers who might be trained in field work here as nowhere else in the world.

---

* There are now meteorological stations, U.S.–manned NATO bases, at a number of places in Greenland.—D.F.

We know that other Danish engineers are quite an article of export; why not add this branch too?

There is just one thing I want to mention right here. When and if Greenland is developed, when and if tourists can go there and enjoy the most beautiful scenery in the world, please let us bear in mind that nature itself can never be restored once it has been brought within the sphere of "progress." On the coast of East Greenland there is a wonderful land. It is the region of Franz Josef Fjord and the adjoining fjords, where mountain peaks pierce the sky, and animals are as yet undisturbed and nature is let alone. Here I want to have a national park established. Let Franz Josef Fjord and the surroundings —as far as the waters run into it—be prohibited for future dwellers or hunters or despoilers of virgin nature.

For us Danes, Greenland means first of all the people. The Greenlanders are by no means Eskimos in the sense of being a "wild" people. Denmark has done a job there to keep the population up, and the policy followed is justified not only by the increase in the number of people, but also by the higher standard of living, far beyond that of any other arctic population. Not everything in Greenland has been ideal. By no means. But everyone has a right to be judged with the background of his own time and education.

It has been a fault that the Greenland administration in Copenhagen has never sent some of its younger employees to Alaska, Hudson Bay, Soviet Siberia, or other places to study. It has been a fault, too, that they have underpaid their employees, with the result that they have had difficulty in educating their children. But let us not dwell on these old shortcomings. A new time is coming. It is here.

The trade monopoly kept up by the Danish government has done much for the natives in Greenland. But
now they have seen other things, they have learned to
know other types of goods, they have found out that
other people look at things in a different way. Greenland
has been opened and can never be closed again without
causing much distress.

Not that I think Greenland should be wide open for
anyone to go there and exploit the people. By no means.
What I ask is that monopoly shall be replaced by the
co-operative trading system which has done so much
for Iceland and which has improved quality and service
all over the world.

The Greenlanders are fit for such a system. Their culture and intelligence are equal to it. If there should be
anyone still who thinks of the Greenlanders as a wild
people, I suggest that he read the report of the last parliament, the *Landsraad,* in Greenland. It shows a council
able to discuss and solve all kinds of problems that may
arise in the country. It is with pride I read that one of
the members of the *Landsraad,* Hans Lynge, gives his
occupation as author. He is an intelligent man filled
with ardent faith in the future of his land.

Fortunately the means of transportation are now so
good that the country no longer needs to be divided into
two separate parts for administrative purposes. Now one
good man at the head would be enough, and this would
put everybody on the same level. Besides, it is helpful to
members of parliament to meet people both from the
north and the south and to learn their special needs.

I know that a co-operative management of trade—import and export—will put the natives in charge of many
affairs where their practical knowledge will be useful.

If in addition some private person should put up a free trading post, it would do no harm.* The volume of production and import is so small in Greenland that no big business can be run without co-operation on the part of the natives.

At present the population is scattered along the far-flung coast, and to meet the needs of the people, there have been no fewer than one hundred and seventy active trading posts. No private company could afford to keep up so many, and yet it must be done in order to care for the well-being of the people. As they live by hunting and fishing it is important, in fact vital, for them to be spread out, for if they were to gather in a few bigger towns, the game would soon be hunted out near the settlements and starvation would result.

Greenland has now become a fishing country. From the days when Dr. Adolf S. Jensen with his famous *Tjalfe* expeditions went there, the fisheries have developed year by year. Formerly the people were poor and had no supplies beyond what they could eat up in a few days. Now the Greenlanders are in possession of seagoing motorboats; they have implements competing with the best in the world and they know how to use them. Poor Greenlanders do not exist any more. In the past thirty years they have learned to build wooden houses. They have abandoned their old skin clothes, or at least wear them only outside of washable woolen ones. This has improved health conditions beyond what could have been hoped.

I remember how in 1910 I met the well-known and most deserving student of health conditions in Green-

---

* The government's monopoly in trading was broken up in 1950.—D.F.

land, Dr. Alfred Bertelsen. He told me then that his goal was to bring the death rate among babies down to twice that of Denmark. That sounded pretty rough to me, until I learned that the death rate among newborn babies at that time was exactly five times what it was in Denmark. Today the death rate is the same in both countries. This shows how the hygienic conditions have improved, thanks to the doctors and the instruction they have given the people.

The Greenlanders are well off compared to what they used to be, but there is still room for improvement. Voices have often been raised to warn both Danes and Greenlanders that the fish, now so abundant along the coast, might find other places to go. What then would happen to all our fishing gear, and how would the people find food?

The answer to this is that we must prepare the fishermen by teaching them to go out in bigger boats, like the Faroe islanders, who sail all the way up to Greenland to fish. In our day the sciences of oceanography and hydrography are so well developed that it is easy to find out where the fish go, and we must put our fishermen in shape to go after them.

The country itself is simply used too little. In the south the sheep farmers have had a certain amount of success, but could do much better. I have seen what can be done in Alaska; at the mouth of the Mackenzie River there are farms, and equally good ones can be developed in Greenland. And we must have tame reindeer up there.* I know the wild caribou is increasing, thanks to game protection. But it is always an advance in culture to own

---

* The reindeer is a domesticated caribou.—D.F.

a herd of animals, so that one can go out and butcher when wanted and as much as is needed, instead of depending on the luck of the chase. Reindeer should find especially favorable conditions in Greenland.

I have been discussing Greenland and its demands at some length. But what about Denmark?

We know Danish trade has had the advantage for many years of delivering goods to Greenland and selling the products brought home. An old law declares that the wares must be sold in Copenhagen at auction. But this system must be abandoned if another pays better. I feel convinced that it has been a good thing for Greenland, in the midst of the disasters caused by the war, that the transportation to and from Greenland has been taken over by young, well-trained shipping men and merchants. They have found, for instance, that it does not pay to send up a steamer and let it call at twelve or more ports; the distribution can better be done by small coastwise boats. They have also learned that the Greenlanders make very fine sailors.

Denmark, we know, is a dairy land. Our income is derived from butter, eggs, and bacon. To produce these things we must have protein, and this must be brought from the outside. Now a Danish-American chemist, Dr. Hebo, one of the greatest authorities on vitamins and protein, has recently visited Greenland, and he says that the Greenland shark contains just what is needed. If we can deliver a sufficient number of sharks, he claims that he can produce half of the amount of protein food required for our cattle and hogs in Denmark. This would give the Greenlanders a fine income and make them important to our Danish farmers.

Yes, I think Greenland has a future such as we never dreamed of.

To every Dane the name of Greenland is dear. Even those who have not seen it feel an affection and interest for the land whose exploration has cost so much, but which has also given brave young Danes their training, and many of us have found our happiness up there.

We all love Greenland. And therefore I know every Dane feels happy and proud that our colony has been of some help to our allies in this war. It has happened before that war and consequent isolation have put Greenland in a difficult position. But this time we had Ambassador Henrik de Kauffmann in Washington and Permanent Secretary Eske Brun in Greenland.

Thanks to Mr. de Kauffmann, Greenland has been supplied with food, and its products have been sold in the United States. What he has been able to do for Denmark will never be forgotten. As for Greenland, he took the situation in hand daringly, as was necessary in dealing with that arctic land. Greenland was saved for Denmark —greater praise can never be given our splendid diplomat in the United States. In Greenland there was Eske Brun who will also be remembered among the foremost names in that country.

We Danes have suffered much during the Nazi occupation. It is our pride that we have not given in. In Greenland they have not done so either, and for this the two great leaders are responsible. No one will deny them full credit.

Peace will come, and Greenland will go back to Denmark—a new Greenland, right on the route to the outside world. It will no more be a closed country, no more be the land of mystery and wild natives. Greenland will wake up, and we have learned that the people are capable of progress. That counts for very much.*

II

In Greenland, recent moderations in an extremely cold climate have brought about changes which give a whole new aspect to this remote land. In fact, it is no longer possible to ignore the importance of this greatest of the world's islands.

Greenland's position on the globe does not alone account for the fact that so few people have ever visited it. Drifting ice prevented easy access, the population was scattered and poor, and Danish policy for many years kept the entire country closed to the outside world.

The present possession of Greenland dates from 1721, when a Norwegian missionary and trader, Hans Egede, managed to fit out a combined trading, whaling, and missionary expedition to the island, believing that the original Norsemen were still to be found there. Centuries before this the Danish king had greatly benefited from his exclusive rights to the land. Then a period of long wars and bad times made it impractical to continue the cost and the risk of shipping, newer markets brought bigger profits to the seagoing Danes, and little by little the colony, and even the sea route, were entirely forgotten.

In 1510 there appeared at Bergen in Norway a ship from Greenland. Sagas relate that this ship was held together by sealskin lines without the use of a single nail.

---

* Time has proved that Peter was right.—D.F.

What later became of it nobody knows; most likely it went down on its homeward voyage. After its visit nothing was heard of the Greenlanders for a long time. Sagas tell of years of terrible weather conditions, with ice drifting in much larger masses, winters that grew colder and longer, and rains so torrential that hay for winter feed could not be dried. But this time was also the time of the Eskimo invasions.

These people coming down from the north, called *skraellings* by the Norsemen, and regarded by them as spectral beings less than human, became more and more aggressive. Battles were frequent, and in 1346 one of the two Norse settlements, the *Vesterbygden,* was conquered. A boat from the south visiting it the following year reported all houses burned, cattle and sheep running wild in the hills, and no living Norseman left. When John Davis went to Greenland in 1585 he found no sign whatever of Norse colonists. By that time the Eskimos had taken possession of the whole coast.

The Eskimos were never numerous, and not even a guess can be made of how many there were, for they traveled up and down the coast constantly in search of food and skins, and it was imperative that they visit the region around Holsteinsborg at least once during their lives to get the huge whales from whose bones they made fishing gear.

Dutch whalers often visited Greenland waters, and several islands, straits, and mountains today bear Dutch names. But the Danish king, having founded a colony, claimed exclusive right to the land. Battles ensued between Danes and Dutch. The latter were finally driven out, and the Danes founded settlements along the coast.

After a few unsuccessful attempts to rent out trading concessions, the Danish government declared a monopoly, closing the island to all but members of the royal trading company so that not even other Danish subjects could be admitted. The last region to be brought inside the monopoly was Thule, where a private trading station was established in 1910. In 1935 Thule was taken over by the state as well.

Over this long period of years the population of Greenland underwent various changes. The *Styrelse* (Danish title for the management of the royal trading company) tried always to keep from altering the native way of life. In the first century and a half their policy was to keep the hunters at their trade. This meant that Danish and Norwegian workmen and sailors were brought into the country to do the work of the colonies and of the whaling stations established on shore. Many of these Europeans took native wives and had children, thereby stamping the population with their own characteristics. This was a blessing to both Danes and Eskimos, for the mixture of European with Eskimo blood produced a stronger, more industrious, more enduring and intelligent people than Greenland had known before.

As soon as colonies were started, strife arose between missionaries and traders, whose viewpoint concerning the natives was naturally opposed. The trading company wanted the population kept scattered, to be wherever the game showed up. The missionaries, on the other hand, desired large settlements where people would at all times be close to church and school. Basic elements resolved this strife. If too many hunters stayed together in one spot, the game in that region would soon be killed off or frightened away, and that would never do. Consequently trading stations were scattered about— some of them at quite considerable economic loss.

A fact never to be forgotten is that the Danish government has at no time selfishly exploited Greenland. What was done, was done for the benefit of the natives. It may truthfully be said that for many years Greenland was the home of a contented and a happy people.

But the very favorableness of living conditions fostered an increase in population that began to overtax the resources of the land. And when, along with discovery of the Polar Current, competition in seal hunting came to the natives from outside, serious trouble developed.

The east coast of Greenland is nearly always blockaded by immense masses of ice that drift down through the Denmark Strait between Iceland and Greenland. It has been known since the time of the Norsemen that Greenland fjords are always full of driftwood—in early days the Eskimos had wood aplenty. The Norwegian explorer Fritjof Nansen, who had already crossed Greenland's icecap, became curious about this drift. When he heard that clothing, utensils, and a boat belonging to the unfortunate *Jeannette* Expedition under deLong had been found by Eskimos on an icepan close to the west coast of Greenland, he realized that these items, abandoned by the Americans close to Siberia's northern coast, must have drifted across the North Pole, south around Cape Farewell, and up along Greenland's west coast. He fitted out his famous *Fram* Expedition, sailed east along the Siberian coast, and then let himself drift with the ice toward the north. He did not go far enough east to cross the pole, but his expedition was the basis for later oceanographic research—and we now know something of the Polar Current.

The natives of Greenland suffered as a result of Nansen's expedition. Large quantities of seals (*Phoca Groenlandica*) were discovered east of Greenland, giving birth to their cubs on the ice. Hearing of this, Norwegian sealing vessels at once set out in fleets to catch the seals before the young ones should be able to swim. These seals were taken by the thousands—and the west Greenlanders saw their supply of game diminish. They, of course, had to stay at home and wait for the seals to come around Cape Farewell in the spring and fall of the year.

By the beginning of this century, fewer and fewer seals were available in Greenland. The amount caught by the natives could never have made any appreciable difference in the supply, but the Norwegians had taken terrible toll. Natives in the southern part of Greenland, entirely dependent upon sealhunting, began to suffer badly. Fish were not so plentiful there, and poverty arose to torture the helpless people. Denmark took care of them, but it is never good for a whole population to live on charity.

As long as the sealhunting remained good farther north, there was no cause for alarm for the country as a whole. But here also came disaster. The moderation in temperature began, causing a further scarcity of seals.

To offset all this, the industrious Danes employed by the *Styrelse* tried introducing new industries. As these proved useful they were taken over by the monopoly. In time quite a number of the natives were able to provide themselves with an income by making rugs and blankets out of eiderduck or other bird skins. The groundshark was productively hunted for the oil which its liver contains. Some fish were salted down and sent to the motherland, some others smoked and sold in Europe for good prices.

But man cannot live by bread alone—and now, though the worst hardships caused by the scarcity of seals had been put at bay, the people began to feel wounded in their self-respect. In early times, only the sealhunter was regarded as a man of true dignity. Those who, for one reason or another, were unable to go out in kayaks to hunt, and had to fish for a living, were looked down upon—had, so to speak, no standing. Now, as the seals disappeared and the colonies grew, there seemed less and less place for a man's pride. Sailors and workmen were recruited increasingly from the ranks of the natives, and the church also employed many. The sons of such men had not even the chance to learn to use a kayak and this state of affairs caused a feeling of shame. By the turn of the century it had become so intolerable to the people that they began to assert themselves. In 1912 they obtained a native democratic constitution, with two kinds of councils—a municipal council of thirty-six members which took care of local affairs, and two provincial councils, one for North and one for South Greenland. Self-government enormously helped self-respect, and during the years the Eskimo has become most clever both in debating and in deciding problems.

The country itself, however, grew poorer and poorer. Then the Danish scientist Adolf Jensen discovered in the southern fjords the presence of quantities of fish never known to exist there before. Much research followed his report, with the result that stations were built along the coast for the purpose of teaching the natives, first how to fish with long lines and nets, and then how to clean and salt and prepare the fish for export.

So began what is now Greenland's major occupation, fishing, with the codfish its chief source. The cod is being found yearly farther and farther north. Every year some new municipal council demands the right to sell it, and asks for saltmasters and leaders. Motorboats, as many as the Danish ships can carry, are given to the natives on credit. Due to the good teaching they have had, and most of all to their own natural integrity, Greenland fishermen have shown themselves fully capable of working these boats, paying for them in full, and year after year buying more. Some hunters still exist, of course, and they are held in high esteem. But they are low in money. They furnish the fishermen with meat and skins, but only very recently have they been able to grasp the fact that one should accept pay for meat. In the old days—and still in the northernmost districts—meat belonged, so to speak, to everyone. It is hard for people with such a tradition to break it, to realize that their land is now no longer a "meat-country," but a "money-country."

The Danish government has long had its attention fixed on the land as well as on the sea. From time to time during the past, Danes brought a few cows to the southern colonies and had milk and meat from them. However, these attempts never amounted to much. But in time a certain old colony trader, named Anders Olsen, settled down, upon leaving his official duties, to farm in the very spot where the Norsemen had had their cathedral and bishopric. Igaligo is the name of the place today— the Norsemen called it Gardar. Anders Olsen married an

Eskimo, and they had many children. All his sons became big strong fellows who followed in their father's
steps, remaining in the fjord isolated from the coast
people. Today the numerous descendants of Anders
Olsen still live there, and are well-to-do people. But they
are no longer the only ones of their kind.

The Danes founded a farming school at Julianehaab,
where it was soon found that sheep make the best stock
for Greenland. At first there was some doubt as to
whether an Eskimo, conditioned to hunting and killing
animals, could adapt himself to the idea of raising them.
This doubt has been wholly resolved. Today, all the
places formerly worked by the Norsemen have been
taken over by Greenland homesteaders. With their superior knowledge and equipment they are able to do
much better than the old Vikings could, and now live
prosperous lives in South Greenland, with money in the
savings banks, larger and larger stocks of animals, and
gardens which produce potatoes, beets, and a variety of
other vegetables. These farmers supply much of the meat
which is needed in the northern fishing communities
where people get tired of eating fish day in and day out,
and where, though some birds are always to be had and
groceries may be bought at the stores, fresh meat will
always be an essential.

Thus to fish and to farm have become the main occu-
pations of a people bred by centuries to live by hunting.
Obviously, such drastic and comparatively sudden
changes in the habits of an entire people call for en-
vironmental adjustments that cannot be made overnight.

Today there are many too many settlements along the

Greenland coast. Some of these have already disintegrated for various reasons. The war put an end to a number in the south. Mr. Eske Brun, known as the "New Father of Greenland" (and since January of 1949 director of the Greenland *Styrelse*) found it impossible during the war years to get transportation for food for people in the south. Something had to be done, and he moved these people north. They are now, all of them, living in a region where starvation is known only by name; and though the old people still talk of their wonderful places down south, remembering sun and mild weather, berries, and bear hunting and an abundance of seal blubber, the younger ones recall childhood spent amid poverty and hunger, and have no desire to return.

It is difficult to realize how recently, in what a few brief years of Greenland's long history, her life has completely changed. It is only a short time since Mr. Brun moved the southern natives into the north—and yet in this time the whole picture has altered. When these settlements were first made, during the war, primitive ways of life still directed thought and action. Sites were chosen on the basis of where hunting was good; tents were pitched and winter houses built where it would be easy to put a kayak and an umiak to sea. A man returning from hunting carried his boat on his back and placed it on a scaffold out of reach of his dogs, as he always had.

Today all is changed. In the south, the seals have disappeared and fish have come in great numbers. Trade has multiplied in volume many times. These "new" settlements, with their stores, churches, and schools added by colonizing Danes, are now so out-of-date and inadequate as to be almost useless.

It is no longer a matter of carrying light skinboats on one's back, but rather of heavy wooden fishing craft which must be dragged up the shore, or left in the sea, of power boats moored outside dwellings, of a need for safe harbors.

Now, suddenly, equipment of all kinds is needed. In the old days—that is, in the days just before the last war —everybody in a community helped unload any ship that brought a cargo into its harbor. All else was dropped when a vessel appeared. But nowhere now is a ship a rare sight—motorboats run in and out daily all along the coast, vessels arrive frequently from Denmark laden with oil, coal, and other cargoes. In my first Greenland days sails were used, and time did not much matter. If the captain took a notion to stay an extra day or two, it was up to him—ships made only one or two trips a year between Greenland and Copenhagen then. But things have speeded up in the arctic as elsewhere in the world. Crews have to be paid, ships must be serviced in a hurry. Loading gear must be provided, and quays built.

In those so recent old days, the Greenlander had his kayak, his harpoons and his spears, and not much else. Now his increased earning power allows him to buy not only food at the store, but also lumber for his house, glass for its windows, coal stoves, furniture—everything that the rest of the world likes to buy.

Greenland's 830,000 square miles make her the biggest island in the world, but less than fifteen per cent of it is habitable—eighty-four per cent lies under the great icecap. It is also the northernmost country on the globe, extending from the 60th to the 86th degree North Latitude—it is easy enough to see why things are "different" in Greenland! But the Eskimo is no longer a wild man, without knowledge of the outside world. The Greenland radio tells him about it, and he sees it more and more at his own door. He met and liked the American soldiers, who turned out to be nice friendly fellows. Each summer strange ships bring thousands of Portuguese and French to his shores. His children are educated in good schools, as Danish youngsters are, with secondary schools carrying on the work of the lower grades. He knows that his country is of great meteorological importance to the world, and he sees his boys and girls being trained as telegraphers and meteorological observers. In short, the Eskimo is entering his larger sphere of life as fast as he can—and so far has never disappointed any hope.

Inwardly the Greenlander has felt uneasy about the changing climate of his land, which each year brings forth the cry, "The codfish came up to there—now they are up to here!" He cannot see clearly what the future holds in store. This the Danish scientists are trying to help him find out.

Dr. Morten Porsild, the famous botanist, has spent a lifetime studying not only this particular island but the whole arctic region, his work resulting in information of great value. The zoologist Dr. Poul Hansen's research with regard to codfish may have contributed more than anything else to the land's rescue from possible starvation. The Danish geologist and arctic explorer, Dr. Lauge Koch, stated in a report that extensive lead deposits had been found on the east coast of the island.* Greenland's cryolite mine, the only one of its kind in the world, has

---

* The lead mine at Mesters Vig has been operating for a number of years. —D.F.

proved profitable for years, half of its earnings going by law to the natives—each person represents a co-owner of the mine—being used to keep up the hospitals, churches, and schools. But it is not known how much can still be expected of this mine; the cryolite may run out, or its use become obsolete, which would be in the nature of a calamity for both Greenlanders and Danes. Dr. Koch was in Greenland (1949–51) trying to determine whether lead may prove a new source of wealth for the natives, and an aid to the loyal little motherland that has spent so generously in building up Greenland and securing her people from want.

On the whole it appears that the great basic elements of change in Greenland life are working together for future good, with a changing climate at the bottom of it all. It seemed disastrous when the warming of the water caused the seals to disappear, but it brought the fish, and they provide money. Money is the source and the need of progress, and progress is well under way.

There is a plan for the development of Greenland, the main requirements of which are four:

1. Quays for ships and sheltered harbors for motor-boats.
2. Cleared lots for buildings, with streets and roads between them.
3. A supply of fresh water for use in houses at all times.
4. Electricity for light and other needs of workshops and homes.

Each new small town will comprise three to four thousand inhabitants. Each will need schools and churches, stores and packing houses, movie theaters and libraries, clubhouses and dancing places—in short, all that one expects to find in any modern small town anywhere. Had it not been for the wartime scarcity of materials, much would have been accomplished along these lines already. As it is the work goes slowly. But the program is there and the earnest resolve to see it through.

The day is past when the Greenlander was a hunter depending on his skinboat, his harpoons and spears. The day now at hand is a momentous one, for it means no less than the introduction of a whole new country into the society of nations, each of whom must take care of some part of human life and happiness if we are to have peace.

Greenland can contribute much to the world, and she will. To predict how much, and in how many ways she will is beyond the scope of this chapter. But one thing is certain. New times are coming to Greenland, and Greenland will know how to take them.

VI.

ICELAND

I.

Iceland: The Ideal Vacationland

Do you like to swim and fish, climb beautiful mountains, go boating in some of the world's best harbors and fjords, and see some of the strangest things of nature at firsthand? Then Iceland is the place where you must spend a vacation. I am surprised that so many young people like to lie on the beaches and soak up the sun. This type of inactive life is fine, but there are other even more rewarding ways to enjoy life.

All I mean to say is that Iceland has it all over the South as a vacationland, and I am sure that people will some day realize it. This of course expresses my personal view, which could be mistaken. But many times people have been surprised to find out that Iceland is not an iceberg but has a moderate, healthy, and invigorating temperature. Its climate is naturally affected by the ocean: the occasional drifts of ice in April and May causing cold, storms, and fog; and the seawinds of the south bringing squalls and cyclonic storms of varying intensity.

But there are warm springs in the interior of Iceland, particularly in the western portion of the southern lowlands. The famous *Geysir* is located there and thousands of people go to visit it. There are also acid springs in the dry highlands of the volcanic districts. Alkaline springs occur on low land at the foot of hills, or at the bottom of lakes and rivers. Some of these last only a day but others endure for hundreds of years, with the water at the surface sometimes two or three degrees above the boiling point. Sulfur springs and boiling mud lakes also exist.

All these springs result from the volcanic rocks out of which Iceland has been formed. Iceland in fact is still among the most volcanic regions of the earth, having more than twenty-five volcanic vents which have erupted and more than a hundred and seven which could. But this is nothing for the traveler to worry about. Actually he may feel disappointed if there is not an eruption for him to tell the folks back home about. Lava streams form some of the most attractive sights one could hope for, and you are lucky if you see some while you are there. You will also be lucky to taste some of the bananas home grown in Icelandic greenhouses which are heated by the hot water piped from the island's natural hot-water systems.

You would also have to see the glaciers and snowfields to make a trip to Iceland complete. These are found mainly in the interior tableland. They sometimes have tremendous proportions not only in depth but in area. Vatnajökull, for instance, covers an area of almost 4,000 square miles, but the others are only about a quarter that size. With these huge fields of billowy snow and ice there is mixed a milky white, or sometimes yellowish-brown clay which runs down valleys and dyes the streams and rivers. And when it runs it sometimes does so with all its might, causing a torrent where yesterday there was a road and where there will be one again tomorrow.

Iceland also has a great number of lakes, some of them with glacial origins or bases. The largest are Thingvallarvatn and Thorsvatn, each with an area of about twenty-five square miles. These waters are filled with all kinds of waterfowl, especially ducks and wild geese—the first discoverers of Iceland, since it was these that were followed by Irish monks and Norse pirates when they wanted to reach land.

I can think of a hundred ways that Iceland is a vacationland. Among the many birds which people like to watch are the snow bunting and the now decreasing Iceland falcon and various kinds of divers, ducks, and grebes. Many enjoy stone collecting, and special stones like liparite and gabbro cannot be procured elsewhere. The food in Iceland is excellent, among the best in the world—at least for visitors. Icelandic cod and herring, cooked in native fashion and served piping hot, will make the traveler return. The trout fishing has long been famous. And the people of Iceland—the simple, trusting, friendly, reserved people who have always been so warmhearted to me—are among the finest on earth.

Iceland is good for soul and body, and if I had my pick of places to spend a vacation, I would not hesitate to make it my choice.

2.

The Woman's Boulder

A MAN'S NAME WAS GRIM. He lived with his father and mother and helped them summer and winter. He was an only child. His father was weak since he was struck in the legs by an avalanche from the mountains, so Grim could not be absent from home for a long time. He did all the work that was heavy on the place and Bergbu had its fields scattered far around. On very steep and winding paths he had to climb to the upper *saeters* to cut the grass in the springtime. There was a small house, put together with big, heavy stones. Grim often wondered how strong those people of old must have been who had built the little house so high in the mountains. He slept there while he was cutting the grass, and when it was cut, he waited until the hay was dry, and went down again. Always much was to be done, because his father could not manage to do hard work.

He worked, but often he saw travelers pass by, but rarely did they call in at Bergbu. They all knew that no great treat was to be expected here. A sick man, an old woman, and a son—shy and embarrassed because he seldom saw people and did not know how to talk to them.

Neither could he join the people who rode to Ting-vellir every year because he did not have people at home to take care of the chores. It happened that some of the passers-by called in, and told him to follow up and vote for certain things which they claimed to be important. Grim wanted to go, but he knew it was impossible. He did not understand the problems—and so he just turned his back and said, "I am not going," without an explanation.

The strangers were served food and treated in a friendly manner. When it happened that they slept over, Grim placed himself in a corner of the room and listened to their talk and this gave him many things to ponder when he was alone.

When the time came to bring the hay down, he took all the horses up through a narrow cliff. He had to help each of them climb the steep terraces and then they moved up where he had his hay. He loaded the horses, but three times he had to take off the hay on the way down, as big boulders had fallen, making the path so narrow that a horse could not go between them while carrying a burden.

So Grim grew to be a tall man, and his light, yellow beard waved in the wind. His hair was long and beautiful and frequently he combed it in case some strangers might come along, and he wanted to make a favorable impression.

When his father died, it did not put much more of a strain on him because in the last years he had been of little help on the farm. They brought him down to the church and the *sira* made a long speech. The neighbors were informed, and Grim's father was buried. Two days

later they were home again and many words were not
spoken between him and his mother.

When the winter was over and the snow melting,
Grim's mother spoke:

"It feels as though one will soon follow the dead man,"
she said. "New clothes are made for you. Take Bruna
and a packhorse and go down to Svinanaes and see Valgerda. She is marriageable, and she is said to be good for
all work. She will be good for giving you many sons
which are needed on this place."

Grim didn't answer, and for many days nothing more
was said about it. Now it is to be told that Bergbu was
situated right beneath Ingolfjalla, and each spring great
boulders fell down from the steep cliff. Sometimes it
sounded like thunder, sometimes it was just like someone laughing, high in the mountains when small stones
and gravel slid down, rippling until they found a place
to rest at the foot of the mountain.

The sheep had been driven out—the lambs were big
enough to follow their mothers. Besides, there wasn't
much hay left for them in the barn. Sheep are clever at
spreading over wide distances and even though the grass
and the herbs are young, and the buds on the willows
and birches still small, there is much strength in the
young sprouts. So the lambs grow quickly, and every
day they wander over the mountains, not to be seen again
before they are driven home in the fall.

Grim arose early one morning. The mother had seen
him brushing Bruna for some days. He had also smeared
his saddle with tallow and combed his hair. She now
took down from the smoke pipe a couple of sheep's quarters and placed them on the table, and brought forward

the old sealskin bag to put on the packhorse when something which must not be spoiled by rain was to be
carried.

No words were said between them, but Grim ate his
breakfast and took his baggage and left.

It felt wonderful to be on the road and he made
Bruna trot over the wide, flat land. When he came to the
mountains he wondered why he had stayed at home so
long. Now he knew the desire to go on—right to the coast
and find a ship to go into the wide world, leaving Iceland
behind, and seeing how other people lived. That night
he came to people he knew only slightly, but he had
heard what sagas had taken place here, and he talked
about it with his hosts. When they had eaten, dried fish
was brought in to be nibbled as a pastime, with unsalted
butter—and he suddenly was enjoying conversation with
people, and he told them about himself and his life.

The next morning, he was up early and before evening he reached Svinanaes. This was a big farm. People
came and went through the doors. Horses were tied up
at the *tun* and there were so many that it didn't cause
much commotion when Grim arrived with his two horses.
A young man came and helped him and offered to carry
his luggage if he expected to stay over until the next day.

Grim said that he had brought food enough along so
he did not need hospitality. This was accepted as a token
that he would be glad to stay over the night. Everyone
thought the young, tall man with the beautiful beard
and the long hair looked strong and handsome. The man
of the house was called Karke, and he did not ask Grim
from where he came, but he was a wise man, so he
talked in such a way that Grim was forced to tell much,

and Karke soon knew about him, and also understood what Grim had come for.

Valgerda was a distant relative. She had been raised in Karke's house, and his wife Helga had taught her all the housewife's duties so that a man would be well-served when he would take her for his wife. Some elderly men, visiting Karke, talked together of things that Grim knew nothing about. It was about Iceland and its desire to come in closer contact with the outside world. They said that someone should persuade the king to send more ships to Iceland. People wanted bread, and grain was scarce. So few ships arrived and when the king was occupied with war in foreign countries, which the people had nothing to do with, the ships stayed away entirely and only a few things could be had in the stores.

Grim was not used to buying much in the stores. Once a year they went after flour. They also bought salt, but that was all. Everything else was made at home and though his tools were old and worn he could use them for many years to come.

In the next days, Grim helped the men with different work. Huge stones had to be removed and he proved himself stronger than any other on the place. In the evenings the young men amused themselves doing *glima* and all the women came out to watch. The victor in each match was challenged by a new man and in the end Grim stood alone. All the rest of the men had been thrown down, some of them complaining of pains in their backs from having been thrown to the ground rather violently. When the wrestling was over, Karke went to Grim and said that he would like to wrestle him himself, as he had once been the strongest man in that part of the country.

"At that time I won Helga, my wife, but as I am older than you, I might be somewhat weaker. On the other hand, I have more experience than you. I notice that your footwork is not very clever. You depend too much on your strong arms."

Grim did not answer but grabbed at the side of Karke's pants and tried to tumble him over. Soon he felt tired, having been through so many fights, but he was stronger than Karke. Time and again he lifted him up in the air but when he tried to turn him over to put him down on the ground, Karke always had a leg preventing him from falling. For a long time they wrestled and finally Karke gave up.

"I can't drop you because you are too strong, and you can't drop me because I know the game, but I know you came here after Valgerda. Your *glima* has given you the right to pick the girl you want."

Grim thought that he was well-rewarded for the strenuous day. In the evening the arrangements were made and Grim told them that his mother was alone at home and she could not manage too long without him, so they should leave as soon as possible.

"That doesn't give Valgerda a big wedding. But she gets a good husband."

The next day the many guests signed their names as witnesses, and Karke gave the newlyweds five horses, and two young men were to follow Valgerda to her new home. Grim had explained that two more hands would enable him to do so much more work and he could go away to the council at Tingvellir and meet other people. They would go trading, and he told her of the fields far up in the mountains from where they could look right out to sea and far, far up over the glacier.

When they came to the farmer on the way home, Valgerda was talking the whole evening with the women. Grim sat beside the man of the house—two married men talking to each other—telling one another about the horses, the sheep, and the cows.

The two hands had already explained that Grim had won his wife in *glima* and everyone was honored at having such a guest and said that it reminded them of days of old when people were strong.

The old woman had prepared everything for Grim's return. She had managed to milk the cows and had churned butter. Milk was put up to sour so she could have *skyr* for him on his return.

Now he came, with three companions, and Valgerda brought bread and blood sausage which had been soaked in sour milk. She also had pots and many utensils, given her by Karke's wife and the other women. Valgerda was fair-haired and mild. She liked to laugh, and before she talked she always smiled.

The summer passed quickly. Valgerda followed Grim up in the mountains and they stayed there until the hay was dry, when they went down for the horses. When fall came, she stayed home with Grim's mother and the three men went up in the high mountains after the sheep. As usual they met men and girls from other farms and it took them more than a month to drive the sheep down to the place where they should be sorted out. Grim was a married man now and he looked with a smile at the young boys and girls when they played during the night while drifting the sheep down the slopes. He knew that when he came to the place, he would send one of the boys home to fetch Valgerda so that she could come and take part in the merrymaking, when all the neighbors got together.

Stallion fights and *glima*. Also trading and bartering. And young people becoming betrothed.

The young man came back alone the following day, bringing word from Valgerda that Grim's mother was sick and was unable to manage herself—not to speak of the cattle and other chores. Said Grim; "For once one's mother has darkened the days for her son."

He hurried, sorting out his sheep, earmarking those lambs not to be butchered, and taking his horse, he rode home, telling the two boys to come after with the herd.

A short time later Grim's mother died. Nothing more happened that winter on Bergbu. Several times people passed by and they brought a pleasant change from the daily routine for the four people. Everyone was happy to see guests.

When spring was very near, but the snow not quite gone, two men came to Bergbu one evening. They came on foot and said they were shipbuilders on the way north where they heard people were going to build great boats, not only for fishing but also to travel to foreign countries, to bring goods to Iceland, to be independent of what the king chose to have sent.

Grim invited them inside and he placed them next to himself at the table and told Valgerda to bring forward sour mutton and blood sausage. She called him to one side and said to him that she did not like the looks of the men. She seemed to remember having seen them before, and had heard that they were fugitives because of thefts and murders committed in other sections of the country.

Grim returned to his guests without answering her and sat down next to the men who had many things to tell. Grim liked to listen to their stories. Overnight, the men slept in one of the bedplaces and they asked Valgerda if she was frightened of foreign men's lice. "Because we have plenty of them."

Valgerda then told them that she had better light a fire in the bathhouse so that they could clean themselves and kill all the lice in their clothing. The men said they did not want a bath. To this she said that people who were not afraid of showing their bodies naked were preferred. That was what she had always heard. To this the two men said nothing.

The following day the men offered to help with repair work on some of the buildings which had fallen down during the winter. After this they stayed a few days more during which they traveled all over the farm and saw everything.

A forceful gale came up and thunder made great noises, during the night. Grim woke up and saw the two men standing on the floor and asked them why they were up so early.

"The bad weather scared us," one answered. "We heard some of the horses out in the barn."

"Horses are frightened of lightning," Grim said. "Let's go to sleep and wait until the morning." So he turned around next to Valgerda and slept.

When he woke up in the morning the two men were not in the room, so he woke the two boys sleeping at the far end of the room and told them to go and call the two men in, as breakfast would soon be ready. But the two men had gone, had taken Grim's and Valgerda's personal horses and their saddles as well. Also the two best pack-horses were gone. When everything was looked after, it was seen that Grim's best clothing was missing and also many other things, including tools and food.

Grim said that this proved to him that they had been wrong, accepting the two men as guests. Valgerda remarked that the two men had not let her follow them to the bathhouse. "It might be they have been branded at the prison."

To this Grim said nothing but they missed the horses and tools many times during the summer. When he met neighbors he heard that the two men were known as law-breakers and that the king's guardsmen were after them.

Later, Grim understood that the horses had been sold to a man far up north. He said that sometime he would go and get them back again.

The summer went by and when the fall came, an evening saw an old woman walking up toward the house. She was a poor miserable woman who told Valgerda that she walked from place to place helping the women clean their wool and mend the clothing. Valgerda told her to sit down. The woman was famished. She showed Valgerda that her footwear was ruined and her feet were sore because she had walked a long distance.

Valgerda gave her a new pair of shoes made from the hide of a stallion which they had been forced to kill because its leg had been broken. Grim saw the new shoes on the woman's feet, and he said they looked like they had been made for the housewife herself. That night he told Valgerda that he had seen the woman snooping in the attic and Valgerda said that the old woman only wanted to be helpful. "And I could use a helper with so much experience."

Grim did not answer her, and the old woman stayed.

The three men went into the mountains to help gather the sheep, and when at the corral Grim sent for Valgerda. She rode to him, leaving everything to the old woman.

At the sorting-out place of the sheep, there were many amusements—stallion fights and *glima,* and young men racing on foot and on horseback. Grim spent some time talking to other men about events from other parts of the country and from the world outside.

When they returned to Bergbu they heard the cows bellowing from a distance. The house was empty. The old woman had left her old clothes heaped in the middle of the floor, and Valgerda's thick coat was gone. All the clean wool, ready to be spun in the winter, was missing and the woman had also taken a horse and left with as many valuable things she could lay her hands on.

Grim said, "It looks like guests who come with nothing, take much with them. Let strangers stay away from here!"

The winter progressed and Valgerda felt a need of a woman to help her. Grim was lucky with the stock, many animals were to be fed and there was lots of work to do. But the winter passed and several times travelers came by and slept during the night. Once in a snowstorm, a party of many people arrived. The gale lasted for several days and there was much talk. They heard that an old woman had been found dead with wool and dressed in beautiful clothes. She was a known thief who had spent many years in prison. Now she was dead, but none had seen a horse near.

The winter was a severe one and much snow covered the ground, even high in the mountains where it usually blew away. Grim was worried that his hay would not last if spring was too long in coming. So much snow had to melt before the sheep could be led out.

One evening, just after the men had finished the day's work and wanted to go home, Grim saw someone walking toward the house. It was a woman, and she looked rather tired and exhausted, and not very attractive. Evidently she was not an old woman, but she was wrapped in so many rags it was impossible to see much of her. She asked for permission to come in and take shelter for the night.

"Experience has told us to turn strangers away," said Grim, and turned his back.

"For the sake of God and the mother of Jesus, don't turn me away! I am tired and hungry. Hospitality should not be denied by a man who was *glima* king when I last saw him."

Grim stopped, hesitating, but then realized what he had lost twice before because he wanted to help beggars. He told her to leave, there was no use, he would not have her in the house and he would not give her anything to eat.

"Go to the next place. It is not further away than you can see when you go around the bend in the road. There is nothing for you here."

The woman stood for a while and then she screamed at him; "Grim! You think you can turn a poor woman away because you are mighty and your luck has not been broken yet. Beware of disaster!"

In the same moment she said those words, they heard

the rolling of thunder on top of Ingolf Mountain. They both looked up and saw great boulders tumbling down like feathers bouncing down the face of the mountain. Huge rocks broke into small pieces, and when the landslide was over, some of the lesser stones, still larger than a man could lift, came rolling over the *tun*.

Grim saw it happening and was furious. Never had Ingolf Mountain thrown its debris so close, and now the ground was covered with rocks where he had toiled with tufts of grass. Much work undone in a moment.

"It looks like something came your way," the woman said, laughing harshly.

"Go away," Grim shouted. "And don't expect anything from here. Property was stolen from me when I had given shelter. You seem to bring disaster even with your arrival."

"Is there no pity in Grim of Bergbu?" the woman asked.

"Go away!" Grim repeated. And he went into his house.

The woman sat down on a stone for a moment, then she stood up and walked away. One of the young boys, on an errand, saw her far off in the valley as darkness fell over the land. Slowly, slowly the woman walked, and she suddenly felt a pain which she could not overcome. It had started to rain, and down through the valley came a gust of cold wind, bringing hail with it. It came with such strength that she found it impossible to fight the storm. One step she took, and then she turned her back, another step, and a third. Her face stung from the hail and she could hardly see to walk, and with the pain she found it hard to go on.

A little further on she saw what looked like a house—
a place to shelter her—a place to sleep. Her body cried
for rest and the prospect of going inside gave her
strength, so she trudged on. There came a pause in the
storm and now she saw that it was not a farm. There was
but one house, with no promise of food and warmth and
help.

"If it only is shelter out in the field for the sheep, or
a place for the hay. Oh, yes, hay would be wonderful."
She moved once more over the ground, the water splash-
ing about her feet with each step. Maybe there would
be hay in the barn! Then she could lie down and cover
herself and sleep, to rest until the weather turned good.
She no longer felt hunger. Nothing else seemed to matter
but sleep.

It was not a barn. There was no hay. There was no
shelter for sheep or anything else. It was a big boulder,
a stone which had been carried there when the mighty
glacier moved everything in its path. When the ice
thawed away it left its rubbish wherever it chose.

But back of the boulder the wind abated. She stood
for a while, trying to go on, but each time she stepped
from the protection of the boulder the winds hurled rain
and hail at her, till she felt she could stand no more. She
was grateful for that kind, protecting stone, and she lay
beneath it, not to sleep, not to rest, but because she had
no strength to stand up.

Here she gave birth to her child, a poor, miserable
baby born too soon, who whimpered weakly, trying to
cry. The child died, and the mother was so exhausted
that she didn't care. Then she did not know anything
more.

The following night a party of travelers came by. They had faced the hardships of crossing the country. Important business compelled them to journey south before anybody else brought the news they wanted to be the first to tell.

They were making short marches each day, driving themselves from farm to farm, having food enough on their packsaddles, which they offered their hosts while they ate the food provided in the houses. They carried with them polar-bear meat, seldom seen inland, and loaves of bread, a welcome variation from the eternal flatbread on the farms.

Kristmannr was the leader of the group. He was a man who paid the others to follow him, and he traveled with a great bag of money across his saddle. He also brought with him a dog which ran at his horse's heels and was suffering because of the water he had to wade through. The party moved across the ground slowly. Suddenly the dog sensed something and let out a few short barks, making his master look around.

The dog turned his head toward the big boulder, and the men saw something which made them go out of their way to investigate. They found the woman and her child, dead and uncovered. She herself was almost unconscious, unable to move. The men dismounted and tried to comfort her as well as they were able. They thought it dangerous for her to ride horseback, but there was nothing else to do. To tie her across a packhorse would be bad, but this was the only way to carry her.

Kristmannr made them place her in one of the large sheepskin sleeping bags, and they lifted her onto the horse, tying her as securely and gently as possible. The horse had been well loaded, but now its burden was given to another animal, and two men walked alongside to see that she should not fall.

"In less than half a day we will be at Bergbu, and there we can leave the woman with Valgerda. You two men walk slowly with her. We will go ahead and wait for you at Grim's place." And so they went.

Along Ingolf Mountain the valley flattens out for long stretches. The houses are built close beneath the high cliffs, but far enough away to avoid falling rocks. Several farms are now located here, and modern times have seen a road built where automobiles hurry along. When you reach a certain point a great heap of stone is said to cover Grim's house, Bergbu.

When Kristmannr and his followers arrived, they expected to see the houses in the distance. At first they did not worry, their eyes being trained to look at mountains and cliffs, and they would easily distinguish man-made houses with windows and chimneys.

But nothing of the sort was seen. An immense landslide had occurred during the night; stones, gravel, and big boulders mixed with earth and snow had tumbled down over Ingolf Mountain, and had buried Bergbu completely.

There were no houses seen, no man, no woman, no cattle nor tools. Ingolf Mountain had thrown its debris further out than it had ever before, to bury the former *glima* king, the beautiful Valgerda, and all their belongings.

When the men came to the place, they saw tracks leading to a pile of boulders. From all sides it could be seen that people had been working there. Small bits of *tun* were seen, but not the slightest remains of a house. Everything had been buried beneath the avalanche.

"We will have to go on and we will stop when the horses are too tired to carry us further," said Kristmannr. And so they went on.

And here ends the story of Grim and Valgerda and Bergbu.

But when a traveler today passes by, along Ingolf Mountain, he is shown a great boulder, where a poor woman gave birth to her child when she was denied shelter.

VII.

RUSSIA

I.

Help From Mars

SOMETHING WAS HAPPENING up in the Kara-Wara. A
prolonged rumbling rose to thunder, to a sharper sound,
and the echoes rolled away over the Saariselka Mountains toward Russia, like a great deep voice saying, Ah
. . . ah, ha . . . ha . . . ha. The widow, Pekka, climbing a
twisting, stony path up to her home, bent under her
sack of dried reindeer meat, heard the warning from the
Kara-Wara, but with one ear only, as she heard all the
other sounds of the mountains, the steady roar of waterfall, the voices of the trees, a sharp complaint as of pain
as the frost knifed into the dark spruce, the gleaming
birch.

It had been a good summer, the best since Ilmari's
death, partly because the children were almost grown
now, and also because there had been many warm and
sunny days. Pekka remembered the two summers she had
worked in a farmer's house in the valley, but all she
could remember was the mosquitoes, great dark clouds
of them, inescapable. Here at home in the Saariselka
there were no mosquitoes. Pekka had never gone away
again and never would. It was easier to breathe at home.

As she walked with a long, strong stride, her eyes always on the path just ahead of her, her thoughts were of the winter. The brooks were freezing and snow was coming. The sky, which had sunk down to the peaks, and lower, was full of it. But her thoughts were not anxious. It was her happiness to count their store: here was the reindeer meat, sun-dried hard and tough as leather—it would go far, and it had come like a gift. The boy Kaarle, not yet fourteen, had come upon the animal in a rocky gorge, and killed it with a knife through the heart, sure and clever as a man grown, and they had dressed it there.

At home there were the two lambs to be slaughtered, and the cupboard full of hard bread, and barley for porridge, plenty of potatoes, fodder enough for the little horse—he'd not starve—and then finally the cow, and the darling. They were both cows, of course, but one was a cow, and the other was the darling cow. They had had her longer, knew her better. Pekka paused a moment to shift her burden, went on again, very tired now, but not slackening her stride. The brief day was going. Ilmari's children were good children. Of course his children would be clever and strong. Through the winter they would have time to study their books. Pekka was glad the winter was coming; now the children would have time for study. . . . She thought of them calmly, though she had been gone all day. There was the big pot of porridge and plenty of milk.

High up in the peaks of Kara-Wara thunder rolled again, but it was not thunder, and the growling echoes ran across the mountains, repeating five, six times, growing fainter . . . Ah . . . ha . . . ha . . . ha . . . The spirits of the air were disturbed, or it was God's voice? She knew, also, that it was the frost in fissures of the crags, prying them apart.

Pekka paused at a brook, ice-fringed, and lay down flat to drink from it. Yes, she was tired; now she knew she was hungry too. She cut off a bit of the dried meat and began to chew it.

She noted that the rumbling drew nearer, and there was a stir of warning in her mind. She would watch her path and the cliffs above for signs of an avalanche as she went on. Through with eating, she drank again from the brook. Now from somewhere out of sight a stone leaped in a shower of little ones, leaped and struck, sending water flying from the brook, and rolled on with greater and greater bounds down toward the valley. Pekka lay with the water washing over her shoulder. When she tried to move she knew the stone had struck her foot and that she was badly hurt. Confused thoughts took her away from the pain, and for a little while she felt free, untroubled, unburdened, but then a cutting, burning, agony came up through her whole leg from the crushed foot, and she knew she must try to raise herself from the icy water, that this was no place to lie and sleep, with the brook flowing over her, and deep night coming. She pulled herself up, stood on her right foot, and deliberately, though her whole body said no, took a step on her left—and fell face forward into some low, leafless bushes.

She sat up and worked the shoe off her injured foot. She looked at it. The blood ran over the stones, made a little brook parallel to the other. She did not groan, though her breathing was heavy, and her round, red-cheeked face glistened with sweat. She spoke in silence to herself about the dried meat. That was not to be left and lost to some fox or wolf. And she must get home, though home was a mile on up through the woods and the rock-strewn gorges. She ripped long strips from her gray woolen petticoat and bandaged her foot, doing a careful, firm job. Then she started, dragging the heavy sack of meat, made two yards, and fainted. When she came to, she tried again. She knew it was more than a body could stand; she knew also, being one of the Karjalaiset, that there's one effort just beyond the impossible and that up there in the mountains that is the effort that makes the difference and must be made. The people of the Saariselka—the Karjalaiset—are a strong and severe people. Their minds are hard but it is not because they have no feelings that their faces are mostly smooth and stern, unsmiling, above weeping. They are gentle and their hearts tender, but they cannot show it. Bashfully the mother speaks to her own child, shyly, timidly even, the husband draws near to his wife, and though they have words enough they do not wear them out; if silence can possibly do, then let it be silence. So it is with the Karjalaiset, Pekka's folk.

Even in her thoughts Pekka did not now waste words. She would drag herself home. Kaarle would do what was necessary for her while Sihva the girl would run down to the valley for help. The women in the Paavos house would help. As for the rest, for winter, with the Lord's help they would get through it even if she would not be able to walk for a time. How stupid though, to throw money away on herself, having a doctor. The pain was going, thanks to the cold, her wound was freezing, as the cold penetrated the crushed nerves they mercifully went numb. Willing with her last strength to stay awake, Pekka sank away into sleep and lay face down motionless.

When she awoke it was into a sensation of movement about her, of the presence of other life. Wolves? A fox merely? Pekka's hand went slowly to the Finnish knife in its sheath at her belt, and the few inches seemed to be miles. She forgot what her advancing hand was, as if it were some separate living thing, then remembered, grasped the knife. Was she still in a dream? She thought she heard voices, the voices of people, not animals, steps that came nearer, went away. Pekka said the Lord's prayer slowly from beginning to end. Here was no place to encounter folk. What would they be doing? Trees seemed to leap straight up because suddenly lights appeared in the woods and went flashing here and there. Pekka heard the tramp of boots and a confused murmur of men's voices. She sighed, and she smiled, resting her head on her arm again. She was safe, then, for if men were near—men and not wolves or maybe the devil himself—they would help her; folk were born to help each other. She shouted, saying, "Come and help me"; saying who she was and that her foot was crushed by a stone. And she was heard, but the effort had been too much.

She looked up at men when she woke again and tried at once to get up. One of them, with a gentle hand on her shoulder pressed her down. They were strangers and therefore Pekka did not speak first. One of the men lifted her injured foot. That hurt with a new, terrible hurt and Pekka closed her eyes. The men talked among themselves. She saw that they were young, boys really, a few years older than her Kaarle. She heard them, but what they said made no sense. Pekka had heard the

Lapps talk, and more often the *Skolts*. But this was a talk entirely different. Strange as the talk of animals, not one word of it made sense.

"*Badnaia babunka, badnaia babushka,*" they said.

After that, how much later she didn't know, a fire was started close to her, and she began to be warm again. It was wonderful to be taken care of. She could see now that there were four of them and could see their faces in the firelight. They weren't her people, nor Lapps either. They were foreigners; but why should they be up here in the mountains now, at the beginning of winter when snow might be expected any day? When snow came, then you stayed here, that was all there was to it. The day had gone but there was an after light in the sky. Huddled around the fire the foreigners asked her questions in words that made no sense. She watched their faces. One of them she liked best, the fair-haired one, whose cheeks bulged like Kaarle's when he smiled. The others were different, with small eyes, and one of them had great pimples all over his jaw. The fair-haired one cut spruce branches, trimmed them, lashed them together with strips from Pekka's own sack—the one filled with dried meat—and there was a stretcher for her.

"*Ispuska, Ispuska,*" they said. It made no sense. She pointed out the direction of her home. The men smiled and nodded, and carefully, tenderly as women almost, put her on the stretcher, picked it up. It hurt, but it was better than walking. Pekka said to herself that she had not been carried since—since when? Since Ilmari, a bride-groom, had carried her across the threshold of their house. And before that? On her mother's back as her mother worked among the potato plants.

The fair-haired one nodded at her and smiled. She thought, "Folk, even foreigners, are born to help each other," and closed her eyes.

II

The children—Sihva with her silvery hair braided tight around her head, and Kaarle half a head taller than she, gazed round-eyed at the strangers. Inside the house, which was of squared logs, painted red, with small windows in three walls—there was one general room. In a corner was the iron stove on the stone hearth of the big old fireplace, in another corner the beds, like bunks, one above the other. There was a ladder to the low attic where Kaarle slept. Pekka on her bed lay still. She had explained to the children. Sihva would soon start down to the Paavos folk, but now she served the strangers, putting the big porringer on the stove. The crust of the porridge was deliciously brown and thick on the sides and she removed it with a knife, served it out on earthen plates with milk from a wooden pail, and the strange men, who seemed very tall, who thronged the little house, sat down and ate until there was not a scrap left. Kaarle took food to his mother but she could not eat, even though the fair-haired stranger, the one who could smile, nodded at her, urging her, offering her milk.

Kaarle went out to the stable. When he came back the strangers were standing up. One of them took him by his arm, shoved him back toward the door. They all went out, Pekka and little Sihva staring after them, frightened, for in that moment the strangers had slightly changed. They did not ask Kaarle to come out with them, they ordered him to do so. The little house was filled with another, dangerous force.

All the men wanted to see was the stable, as it turned out. The cow and the darling stood there in a fog chewing the cud. Kaarle had cooked *soerpe* in the huge boiler and the fog was steam that filled the whole snug little stable. *Soerpe,* birch twigs with the leaves on, is relished by the cows of the Saariselka—and by a horse, too, if he can get a bit of it. Their little horse, with hair on him long as a bear's—for he foraged for himself through the brief daylight and needed what warmth he could grow for himself—didn't give milk and therefore got no *soerpe,* except when he could. The strangers seemed more interested in the cows, especially the darling, white with big black spots and very fat; they felt her all over and talked in their strange language. They said *korova,* and when they came to the little horse Kaarle heard *loshad,* whatever that meant. Kaarle had never seen a Russian. Though the border wasn't far it had been sealed tight for many more years than he was old, but now as he watched them round-eyed he began to realize they must be Russians. They had got through that border, had escaped. But what did they want with their cows? One had fastened rope about their necks and they pulled at the animals to lead them outside, all four talking at the same time. It was Kaarle's temptation to pull out his sheath knife and go at them, for at once he saw what they were there for—to rob them, but Kaarle also had seen the heavy pistols the strangers carried. He stood silent as the cows were lead out into the little yard, then he went in to his mother.

"They are not good men," he said to her.

She looked at him steadily, her cheeks bright from fever of her wound, and asked, "The cows?"

He nodded.

Without the cows they were done for. The cows were their life, especially just now at the beginning of winter.

"Stay here," Pekka said. "Keep still, watch. Sihva must run down to the Paavos. He will come up in the morning." She whispered, though who of those robbers could understand real language? "Let him bring his son and their guns. If these men go first, you follow them, then later you can show Paavos the way."

The men came in again and sat down on the benches by the heavy table. The fair-haired one brought out pieces of smooth, colored paper. Money, but very strange-looking money. What was it for? He took Kaarle to the window, pointed out at the tethered cows, talked, gestured. He smiled. The other men did not smile. They yawned and spoke impatiently, and fear deepened in the little house. It was a strange thing to Pekka. One moment they were men as other men and then they were not men; they walked through her house as if it were theirs, as they talked they forgot her. She, her children, the house were of no importance to them, almost as if they were not real. The fair-haired one shrugged at last, getting impatient at Kaarle's inability or refusal to understand. He put the paper bills on the table and weighted them down with a wooden butter dish, and they all got up and went out, but from the door one returned and saying something with a bad smile, pocketed the money. Then they were gone.

"What are they doing now, Kaarle?"

"Talking. They look at the sky. It is almost dark. Now

they just look at each other." Kaarle turned away.
"They're putting them back in the stable," he said.
"They've decided to stay till morning. Sihva! Where's
Sihva, Mother?"

Sihva had gone. She was running down a steep accustomed path toward the Paavos in the valley. Too dark
to run as she was running, but she saw the better for
her fear. The old ones told tales of sudden, horrible misfortune like those which had come to them—her mother's
broken foot, then robbers. She ran on, used to running,
for she had tended the animals up and down these
steppes all her life. She felt the first snowflakes on her
cheek and was comforted, and ran on. Let there be plenty
of snow: then they could the more easily trace those
robbers and save the cow and the darling cow.

III

When she came after two hours to Paavos' house, she
dared not go into his gate for the yard was crowded with
strangers, men in great coats, fur caps, fine leather boots.
Were these more robbers? But there was neighbor Paavos
standing among them, talking to them in their own
tongue, in Finnish, pointing this way and that, and Sihva
saw that these men for all their fine boots were Karelians
like herself. She crept in among them and stood near to
Paavos but dared not speak, until he, seeing her, called
out her name and asked her quick, surprised questions.
But what was strangest was that when after telling of her
mother she spoke of the four strangers, they immediately
took her into the house to an officer seated at the Paavos'
big table, and the way he questioned her and all of them

hung on her words was nothing like anything that had ever happened to her before. But she was not stupid; they told her it was war, and she knew what war was, could understand that her news of the first Russians in this district was indeed of great importance.

"So they want your cows for their regiment?" said the officer. "They'll not get them, little one. We'll stop that, and look there!" Sihva looked out the window and saw that it was snowing as she had never seen it snow. The air was solid with it. "Thank God," said the officer. "Thank God," Paavos echoed him.

IV

Pekka lay in torture, her long son beside her, and her thoughts turned round and round that dried meat. Such a good store of it, lost! It was hard to endure that loss. For a time one of the strangers sat near the stove, apparently on guard, the other three all asleep in the hay of the stable. The watch finally uncomfortably sank back onto the bench, began to snore, woke with a start, and struggled to his feet, then started out to join his fellows. He had trouble with the door. Kaarle got up to open it for him.

"It's snowing, Mother," Kaarle said, coming back to bed.

She said, "Thank God," Her thoughts turned round the snow, how it would drift up. She thought if she had her good foot back she might go quietly to the stable and knife the four of them, if she were strong and quick, one after another before they woke. The snow would hide their bodies safe till spring; nobody could find them and take revenge.

But she could not walk.

Kaarle put birch logs in the stove. He was tired out, and she felt as he crept close to her it was as if he were little again. She heard him sleeping. Poor boy, poor little boy, she thought, though he was not little. She lay without moving, her teeth tight together as the ache of her crushed foot throbbed through her.

The moment Kaarle was up in the morning he brought her milk and did what else he could for her. He saw by the shine and unsteadiness of her pale blue eyes that she was very sick, but she was silent about herself.

"Go out," she said. "Watch them."

The snow was deep. It was up to his waist. The house had grown small. The stable was a mound with only the top of its broad door visible. The sky was clear again and the northern lights ran up and down across it.

"Here it is," Kaarle said to himself. "Here we have the great holy winter," and he stood listening to the wonderful silence that filled the world. There was no wind. The forest was silent. The roar of the great waterfall that plunged from the crags above the forest was silent, for it was frozen solid. But the great silence began to be broken by a ridiculous commotion. The stable door resounded like a drum and shook till a flurry of snow fell from the eaves above it. The Russians in there were trying to force the door. The snow was too heavy against it, and they were prisoners. They began to shout. Kaarle answered them. After all, the animals had to be fed, the door would have to be opened in any case. Kaarle went inside and took his skis off their rack by the door. It was good to have them on his feet again. He tried them. Ah, at once it all came back. He went out to the stable door and, with a broad wooden shovel, cleared the drift so it could be opened. They came out, four tall men, blinking in the snow glare, overcoats long as gowns to their ankles, bits of straw all over them, even on their red-starred caps. They had slept like dead men, now they were hungry and angry for having been locked in. They might have struck Kaarle but for the amazing change they found in the world, the very spruces half-buried in snow, and nowhere the sign of road or path. They stood and stared. The sheep, frantic to get out, ran against them. With legs as sharp as sticks the sheep floundered into the dry, light snow. The Russians gazed as one of the sheep dove head first into a drift until only its woolly rump was visible, black feet and quick tail signaling that down below its teeth had found ground level, and lichens to eat. Kaarle, leaving his skis at the door, fed the animals, talked to the darling softly, hope returning to him. For now how could they take the animals away? Soon Sihva would come back with help.

Outside, the Russians were floundering toward the house. They called Kaarle, for they had learned his name at least, and Kaarle went out there, began to shovel. When they got to the house they went in and stood around Pekka's bed talking, making careful gestures, then impatient gestures. Pekka gazed at them, from time to time slightly shaking her head. What was the good? She understood nothing. She understood however that the one who was building up the fire didn't care how much wood he used, and she saw the porridge pot was being emptied and that quantities of warmed milk were being swallowed—milk that should have been frozen and put away for the time when the cows would be giving less and less. Four big men held here by the snow! They would eat up everything! Pekka could understand that. Lying still, her face expressionless, she raged against them, prayed for the arrival of her own people to drive them out before it was too late. They found some cheese and ate that. The fair-haired one came and asked Pekka about her foot, but she did not answer him at all. He offered her warmed milk. She refused. Then he raised his shoulders and clasped his hands together apparently saying he was sorry, or that whatever happened he, at least, could not help it, and his face was anxious and was understandable like that of someone she might know; but in the midst of this, suddenly his eyes went wild and he shouted, "Sihva!" He turned to the others, and there was a rush and gabble of talk.

Now they shouted questions at Pekka, angry and fearful, realizing for the first time the little girl was gone, and Pekka gazed at the ceiling, as if she were made of stone.

"Kaarle!" they shouted. They went out after him and set him to harnessing the shaggy little horse to the sledge. Kaarle was obedient. Where did they come from, what sort of world—these Russians, who would not know that no horse on earth could get them through such a snowfall as this, without men going ahead to make some sort of a roadway with their skis?

Kaarle stood aside with a face as aloof and smooth as a Chinaman's as they started the little horse off. He was willing. He tugged, he floundered into a drift. He sweated. His breath came like the steam from the little engine of the woodcutters down in the valley. Under savage whipping he tried again. At last they gave it up, and Kaarle could put the exhausted horse back in the stable. Kaarle, who wasn't a man yet after all, was crying, but no one saw this. "More snow," Kaarle said to the little horse. "More snow's coming," and patted his heaving sides. Then he built up the fire in the stable stove and cooked *soerpe* for the cows. It was cozy in the stable. The Russians came in and sat down. They watched Kaarle and now he knew that he was in danger: they were cornered and knew it and he must go carefully or they might kill him.

V

A bird whistled on two notes, "Come and find me," the plaintive, faraway call one may hear in the valley or among the highest peaks where there is always snow. That was also their call, Kaarle's and Sihva's. He knew it was she and after a long time went in to give his mother water and say Sihva had returned, then he went out and behind the stable got on his skis. He dropped away across what was the potato patch in summer, to the base of the great rock where he was sure she would be, for that was where they had always played at robbers, and war too. It wasn't play now. From the rock the forest dropped away into a deep cleft between two ridges of the mountain's slope. There were men down there, not just Paavos and his son, but a dozen or more strangers.

Sihva said, "They are soldiers, our soldiers." She told them of the war that had begun, that Finland was invaded. She was different, Sihva was, more important with her important news, and it irritated him a little that it should be she telling him and not the other way about as it was usually.

The officer beckoned him. Standing side by side on their skis he and Kaarle talked. How many Russians? Where had they come from? From what regiment? Hadn't they a number on their collars or armbands? Where were his eyes? And so on till Kaarle, hearing more talk than he would hear usually in a year's time, felt his head spinning. Were they on skis? Kaarle laughed. Now he dared to ask a question. The officer said, "Oh these Russians probably came from some place south in Russia where skis are unknown." That would explain it. That and having donkeys for staff officers!

"Mother's in pain," Kaarle said. "Her foot is bad. It smells bad."

The officer frowned and shook his head. "We'll take care of her," he said. "We'll get her down to a hospital in the morning. But now . . ."

There was a distant shout of, "Kaarle!" The Russians had found him gone. The house door slammed, and slammed again up there, and again the call, "Kaarle!"

Kaarle and the officer crept to the top of the rock. They could see the little house, buried almost to its eaves, and the mound that was the stable, and between them two of the Russians gazing about at nothing, at the snow, white, seeming to glow in the evening dusk. They were black figures, legless in their long coats, but the posture of their arms as they waited for an answer to their shout was a gesture of bewilderment, of blindness. They smelled deadly danger and could not see anything but the snow.

The officer slid back out of sight, beckoned men in white coats to him. They moved silently on their skis, rifles ready. Two started toward the house, crouched, moving slowly. They had been told to take them alive, if they could.

Kaarle on his belly in the snow watched in the dead silence. Sihva beside him hid her face.

Kaarle saw one of the Russians move slowly backward in a circle. He was watching the forest. Now he had his pistol out. Suddenly seeing movement or thinking that he did so he leaned far forward and fired blindly. The shot was loud. On its rolling echoes the steel-string twang-g-g of the bullet sped into the forest. A spruce tree, hit squarely, shook a little cloud of snow from itself. A Finnish rifle spoke. The Russian aiming his pistol—looking here, there, seeing nothing—leaned back against the stable wall, dropped his pistol. He seemed to be resting. He bent his knees slowly, picked his pistol up. Before he could fire there was another rifle shot and, hit again, he fell. Kaarle saw how he thrashed his arms and legs, dying, desperate and helpless as a fox that has been struck a killing blow. Another Russian came out from behind the stable, fired once and again, and again, ducked behind the stable, thrust out again to fire, and two rifles cracked almost at once. As if he had been shoved he stumbled backward. With an odd, deep cry he fell down and at once the snow half covered him.

The officer, back beside Kaarle, cupped his mouth in his mittened hands, bawled: *"Rooki-work, rooki-work!"*

"Means hands up," the officer said to Kaarle.

The stable door opened and the other two came out, bare hands in the air. "You see, they understood." The officer was pleased with himself. "Well, it's over," he said to Kaarle.

"Good," Kaarle said steadily. "Now we are safe. So long as we have the animals we'll be all right this winter."

"What?" The officer looked at him, surprised about something. They had started up to the house. "Oh, yes," absently. "Yes, yes." They went in to see poor Pekka.

Sihva followed.

"I brought help," Sihva said to her mother. "Now you will be soon all right again."

The officer spoke to Pekka. He was not a doctor; he could bring no doctor, but tomorrow they would have her down in the valley and in good hands. He had brought some little white pills that would help the pain if she would be so good as to swallow them. Pekka took the morphia. She could only whisper.

"You were good to come to help us," she said. "We are little people. We are not important."

"It is war," he said.

"Yes, yes, now you shoot each other as when I was small," Pekka whispered. "It makes no sense, not for us little people here, nor for them over there beyond the Kara-wara. But let be," she said. "You have saved us the darling cow, and the cow. We thank you."

She went to sleep and the sound of her heavy breathing and the tick of the wooden clock were the only sounds in the house until they brought the Russians in there to be questioned, the fair-haired one and the one with the red spots on his jaws. It was strange how now the Finnish soldiers acted as if the house were theirs, and stranger still how much alike the questioning Finns and the Russians were, somehow. All were in the same business as it were. The Russians said they had come from Kiev, gave their names and the number of their division; they were in dread of their lives, white-faced, and when they were not speaking stood stiffly, shoulders hunched.

Pekka woke and gazed across the room. The fair-haired one spoke to her, nodding, and the officer, translating, said, "He says it is good you could sleep, little mother. He is sorry he could not help you."

Pekka smiled a little, nodded her head once at the fair-haired one.

But here there was a pistol shot in the yard! The officer did not look up.

Sihva came in, crying like a baby.

They had shot the darling.

Who had? Pekka asked trying to sit up, falling back at once as the pain conquered. She took Sihva's hand. She was utterly bewildered.

The Russians, questioned further, were saying that they had been bound for this very place in fact, when they had come upon the wounded Pekka. Yes, this farm was on their maps. It would make an excellent outpost for observation, situated high up as it was.

The officer, as if unwillingly at last heard Sihva's sobs. He half turned in his chair, said sternly, "We must all leave this place in the morning. We could not take the animals. Soldiers must eat. You will be paid. I will give you papers for everything."

"We've always had her," Sihva said. She could not say how she had loved her. Her tears said something.

Soon the other cow was slaughtered, and the sheep, and then for an hour or more Finnish soldiers cooked a good meal of fresh meat and ate it cheerfully, laughing, sharing with the two Russians.

Pekka was silent. But she had spoken. She would not leave this place. She swore she would not. This was home and she would be out of place anywhere else. She would not know how to act or even breathe down there in the valley. But it was not for her to say, after all. In the morning they started down, Pekka warmly wrapped on the little sledge, the prisoners trudging behind, the ski soldiers ahead beating a roadway. Kaarle went along beside Pekka, talking as he had never been able to talk before.

"You will go to the hospital," he said. "You will have a good doctor and your foot will be made good again. We will have new cows, four instead of two, when the war is over. We will be really prosperous then."

Pekka did not speak.

"Sihva will be with friendly people in a safe place and you will join her," Kaarle said.

"And where will you be?" Pekka spoke at last.

"I? Oh, I will be a soldier in a thick coat and a fur cap and boots as good as theirs," Kaarle said. "I'm big as a man, the officer said so himself, and I will say I am sixteen."

After a while Pekka said, "The sledge is heavy."

"It's carrying a great load of meat beside you," a soldier said.

So that was it.

She had watched them, fed them, protected them from bears. Now they were a pile of frozen meat on a sledge.

"Kaarle, where is Sihva?"

"She is coming. She is coming now."

At the curve in the road there was a great drift, and they must wait while the men ahead skied this way and that trampling down a way for the horse and sledge. Pekka, because the sledge had half turned, could look back and up at her home. As she saw it she did not make a sound, though no one had dared prepare her. Flames red as blood danced and swirled from the roof of their little house. The stable was a torch. Above the flames the black smoke climbed and flew away toward the Kara-wara, and she remembered the hollow and thunderous voice of the new frost in the crags, how it rolled and growled over the mountains, and echoed far away saying, almost, Ah, ah . . . ha . . . ha . . . ha . . . A voice bigger than anything, too big for little people to hear, or to understand . . .

"March," bawled the officer, and they started down again. Sihva caught up and went silently on the other side of the sledge. She did not look at her mother. "All the other houses hereabouts are to go," she said. "We must leave nothing for the Russians." Her little girl's face was bleak. She looked straight ahead. "We must all fight for our country," she said.

But Pekka only knew that from being better prepared for winter than she ever had been—and what was life but preparation for winter?—she was entering this winter with nothing at all, and even homeless. But she did not trouble people with her bewilderment, not the surgeon who operated on her foot, and saved it, though the ankle would never be right, and she would always limp, not the nurses, and certainly not the other homeless ones she met in the barracks of the strange village they finally took her to, for "the duration." Why talk to them? They knew as much themselves.

VIII.

THE FAR
NORTH

I.

Captain Cleveland

My nearest neighbor at Repulse Bay was known only as Captain Cleveland. To the Eskimos he was Sakoart-arnak, meaning "the harpooner." This was because he first came to the arctic as a whaler. Originally from Martha's Vineyard, Captain Cleveland spent his entire life in one frustrating attempt after another to get to China. His ambition was to verify at firsthand some anatomical peculiarity of Chinese women.

This passion first gripped him when he was just a boy of fourteen. Unable to get a berth on a China-bound vessel, he took one that was on its way to Europe. This initial detour seemed to set the pattern for the rest of his life. After his return from Europe he actually bribed a sailor to desert from a ship headed for Asia, so that he might take his place. Unfortunately, at the last minute, new orders came, and the ship went directly to London—which was old and dull stuff for the boy—and from there to the West Indies. Young Cleveland swallowed his disappointment. After all, the largest part of his life was still ahead of him. But his next trip, he swore, would be to China, and nowhere else. As luck would have it, however, ever, he got drunk celebrating his decision, and he ended up, without his papers, in the bottom of an old hulk bound for Boston.

Boston! He spit with disgust. He might just as well have stayed at home. And besides, he couldn't go back to his family with no money in his pocket.

Try and scheme as he did, China just wasn't in the cards for the boy, and one evening he was hit on the head, securely tied, and thrown aboard a whaling ship setting out for Hudson Bay. When he recovered sufficiently, he was put through the usual ritual reserved for shanghaied sailors; that is, he was roundly beaten by the captain, the first mate, and the boatswain, in that order. This was to prove how much they regretted the manner of recruitment. The reception did serve to bring out the best in the lad, and he soon showed himself to be a very able seaman. Ice conditions forced the whaler to prolong its voyage well into the following year, and only when spring arrived were they able to start for home, stuffed to the gunnels with whale oil.

Back in Boston, there was another week of wild celebration, and then the same process started all over again. A dark night, a sudden clout on the head from behind, a few expert knots around his hands and feet, and a dull thud as he hit the bottom of the rowboat that delivered him, more or less intact, to a new whaler. But Cleveland, young as he was, was an old hand at this. Straight away he assured the captain that he considered the whole shanghai procedure great fun, and that he was walking up that street just praying for a clout on the head, and that whaling was exactly his idea of a first-class career for a fellow like himself. Naturally this made him very popular with the skipper, the first mate, and the boat-swain, in that order.

Still too young to command one of the boats, he was permitted to toss the harpoon now and then, and in this he had better luck. Right off he rammed his first bow-head, and the captain began to look upon Cleveland as if he were a walking rabbit's foot. The boy advanced rapidly as a harpooner, a highly paid trade in those days, and his pockets were crammed with dollars now. He was beginning to feel that one day he would really amount to something.

But his main ambition was still to get to China, to investigate for himself the truth about the women there. Some nights he even dreamed about them. These dreams, and the pictures that he bought of Chinese ladies, were pretty much his only contacts with that land. Cleveland never was much for reading, and since he left school he had only signed his name once or twice, getting on or off a ship. He'd have been there long ago, he told me, but destiny intended him for other things. Every time a chance came along to muster on a ship for the East, he got drunk; and then either the police or the shanghai bosses claimed him. Somehow or other he always ended in the same place—the frozen north. Grim old Hudson Bay with harpoons and whales, whales and harpoons.

One break did occur in the cycle, the time his ship was wrecked in the Bay. He was separated from the rest of the crew, and was picked up by a little ketch that be-longed to an outfit that was up there trading with the Eskimos. Cleveland joined them.

Sailing around and visiting the settlements was fun

for a while, and being in charge of a lot of valuable goods gave him a sense of responsibility. Cleveland enjoyed being a big man to the natives. He knew how to apply himself, and he made a nice-sized profit for the company. At the end of his first summer, he took the ketch out through the Straits and down to Labrador to meet the managers of the company. They persuaded him to go back again that same year, and to trade straight through the winter. Cleveland agreed. At Wager Bay he built a small shack for himself and spread the news that he was ready and willing to do business with anybody for anything. Since none of the other companies could get there until the ice broke, he had the field all to himself, and did exceedingly well.

Cleveland stayed on at Wager Bay. The Chinese women still cropped up in his mind occasionally, but there were substantial numbers of local ladies who suited his tastes. Compared to Boston, he freely admitted, native morals were on a lower, but much more agreeable, level. It also built confidence among the natives, he argued, to see that he was not above such relationships. There were quite a few Eskimo boys and girls with unusually large noses running around the camp, testifying to the fruitfulness of Cleveland's policy.

Almost before he knew it seven years had passed, and his company, Lambsom & Hubbard, sold out to the Hudson Bay Company, Cleveland being thrown in with the deal. The new owners dangled a pension under his sizable nose, so he agreed to stay on.

But China stuck in his head. "I'm from Martha's Vineyard," he told me once. "We're not a people to give up after a few disappointments." Another few years and he'd have his pension, and still be young enough to appreciate the sights in that exotic land. Then he would travel, not before the mast, but as a tourist, sitting in a cabin and having waiters bring him drinks. And the girls would have more class than if he went as just another drunken, broken-down sailor. Oh no! Cleveland would reach China, all right. He was just biding his time.

For the time being, however, he was stuck at the northern tip of Hudson Bay. Customers traveled all the way down from Igloolik, through the Fury and Hecla Straits, to his trading post at Repulse Bay. And I was happy, when occasion offered, to make the five-day trip from my own headquarters to visit him. You can learn a lot from a man like Cleveland. Just listening to him bargaining with the natives, for example, made you appreciate how skillful the Eskimos were in guessing what you were trying to tell them; and how careful they were to use only the half-dozen words that they were absolutely sure he understood.

Captain Cleveland and I became good friends. Our common experiences in fighting whales and in trading established a bond between us, and for a little liquor there was nothing that he wouldn't do for me. The liquor was an understandable problem. In those days you were only allowed six bottles a year "for medicinal purposes." Naturally, everyone ordered all six at once, and by the time the boat arrived, months later, there was such an accumulation of ailments that the bottles were emptied immediately. Needless to say, the patients felt much worse by the time the last of the contents were drained, and the prospect of another whole year between drinks blackened their mood for weeks.

And now, suddenly, as though sent from heaven, the Danish expedition arrived with what seemed to be a bottomless amount of liquor—for us Danes, that is; not for captains from Martha's Vineyard. For myself, I didn't care, not being a drinking man. As for the Captain, the mere idea that there was whisky somewhere in the Northern Hemisphere brightened his world considerably.

In Greenland, where I lived, there was an old custom called *flaskefoer,* which required that a few bottles be kept in the sled when going on a visit. When you arrived at someone's house, the host was obliged to refill the portion that was consumed on the trip. Those hospitable days are gone now, but I continued the custom, not wishing to publicize how low my country had fallen in its behavior. So I always appeared at Captain Cleveland's with *flaskefoer,* and right from the start he was very enthusiastic about this tradition. Of course, he told me, I must understand that political corruption in Canada kept him from refilling my bottles, but he would certainly join in a toast to the good health of the expedition, to the king, to me—in short, to everything, so long as we toasted them separately.

Such a neighbor is wonderful to have, and we managed to make our friendship mutually profitable. My goods, with which I paid the natives, were not better than Captain Cleveland's, but they were different, and much appreciated by everyone. It is true that my presence hurt the Captain's business somewhat, but nevertheless he remained very generous, finding crews and dogfood and whatever else I required. In return I brought him gifts whenever I came. In this country it is sound politics to

keep on the good side of a man like Cleveland, particularly since our Greenland Eskimos, who are much better
hunters than the Hudson Bay natives, had cleaned out
all the caribou from Vansittart Island. It would take
many years to restock that area again, and occasionally a
man develops a terrible craving for a juicy piece of caribou meat. There were plenty of caribou in Captain
Cleveland's neck of the woods.

Whenever I asked him what he would like me to bring
him, he always answered, "Three of anything. Whatever
you send me, never send one alone. Always three. If one
of these terrible girls who hang around me sees that another gets a kettle, she will make life a hell for me until
I give her one also. It's awful, awful. Remember, I don't
care what it is, so long as there are three of it."

This one year that I write about, the Captain and I
agreed to celebrate Christmas together, and again I asked
him what he would like. Just three of anything that I
could lay my hands on, he said, once more going into his
grievances against the women. "But for myself, just something to drink. Christmas isn't Christmas unless you can
drink a cheerful toast to it. No, I have no favorites. Any
kind of whisky will do."

If these were my friend's wishes, I was determined to
satisfy them. I gathered together as many bottles as I
could from my own ration, and from some of the boys
who stayed at my post. I also invited two learned scientists, anthropologists studying the ways of the Eskimo,
to accompany me on the trip. They had never been so
far from my headquarters before, and they wanted to
have some experience in traveling by dogsled. They were
looking forward to meeting the famous Captain Cleve-

land, who, they hoped, might share his knowledge of the natives with them. They were weighed down with packages and letters that they were going to open on Christmas night, but they had nothing to give the host, so I was quite certain to make the best impression. When Christmas was less than a week away, we packed ourselves into all kinds of skins and took off with our teams in the darkness.

The trip went well, and the anthropologists turned out to be surprisingly good travelers. At the end of five days we pulled up outside of Captain Cleveland's quarters. He gave us a warm welcome and made us very much at home, but he lost no time in telling us how sad it was not to celebrate the night before Christmas with a traditional cup of coffee and whisky, "just by way of greeting the holy season, you know. Coffee and whisky. It's an old custom back at the Vineyard. Somehow it doesn't seem at all like Christmas without it. By the way, don't you think we'd better bring those bottles in from the sled before they bust wide open from the cold?"

I assured him that there was good whisky in those bottles, and not even the frost of an arctic winter could stiffen this stuff. But nevertheless, the Captain kept harping on the subject until I let him bring one bottle in. Then, of course, he had to test it, "to see that the trip didn't spoil it. Terrible things can happen to whisky that's been jogging over the ice for a week. People don't appreciate what delicate goods whisky is. Besides, I want to make sure this is the same stuff we used for Christmas back home." Strange how sentimental the Captain became about Martha's Vineyard whenever whisky was mentioned. He had to test it several times before he was absolutely certain that it would meet the high standards set by the natives of Massachusetts.

The scientists were exhausted from the journey and wanted only to climb into their bags and sleep for two weeks. They turned in right away. I was pretty bushed myself—to use Captain Cleveland's expression—but it was ill-mannered to pass out on my host so soon after arriving. Cleveland rambled on for a bit about this and that, about my not being a drinking man, and how he was willing to forgive me this failing. "We all have our weak spots," he observed, sadly shaking his large muskox head. Then he called the lady who happened to be in favor at the time. Her name was Fatty, and she was pretty handy with a bottle herself. Soon they were singing and dancing and filled with all-around good feeling.

But when the bottle was empty I refused to open another. Enough was enough. Before we turned in, though, Cleveland had to tell me all about his love for Denmark, and for the royal family, and most of all, for me.

"Tomorrow night I am going to treat you to a ten-course dinner, no more and no less. Ten courses of food like you never ate before."

"Only a little caribou meat would be fine," I protested. "We have very modest appetites."

"Nope. Ten courses or none." That was the ultimatum, and on that I toppled off to sleep, but not before I heard him arguing with his girl. She swigged too hard at the bottle, he complained, in his awkward, broken speech. It wasn't ladylike. He should have called one of the other girls instead, and tomorrow she would get nothing at all. Nothing. Fatty's response was delivered in choice Eskimo idioms that were truly, by our standards anyhow, most unladylike.

In the morning Cleveland awoke with a "sore throat." Also, he reminded us, in Canada "which is where we are now," gifts are always distributed on the morning of Christmas Eve. He would have given us ours now—if he had anything to give us. But he didn't have anything. Everything belonged to that damned Hudson Bay that kept him here year after year without so much as a jigger of whisky to help celebrate the birth of the Christ child. He stuck on this theme so long that finally I gave him another bottle.

"I'll just take a little drink now, an eye opener, and hide the rest of it away so Fatty won't get her mitts on it. Once she sees it, the bottle is dead. Dead and buried. And then the other girls'll hear about it, and all hell will break loose."

I reminded him that the bottles were still mine. That was a mistake.

"In that case, I better take care of them for you. You know how these Eskimos are about strangers. That box isn't safe out there on the sled."

He carried on and on like this until he wore me out and I turned over the entire box to him, to dispose of as he wished. After all, I did bring them for him.

"And by the way, about dinner," I told him. "Ten courses are far too many. And too much work. Think of all the dishes we'll have to wash." But it was like trying to halt an ice floe.

"Nobody from Martha's Vineyard ever goes back on

his word," he roared. "I said ten courses, and ten it's
going to be. No more, no less."

Five minutes later he was back from the kitchen. Unfortunately, there was nothing with which to make the
last course, "but nine different dishes ought to be something worth sitting down for. And believe me, I'm man
enough to swing that."

We could hear him calling his girl, but not the one
from the previous night. In another minute there was
a full-scale battle going on with the three ladies fighting
for the bottle. Captain Cleveland was gracious enough to
toast all three of them, individually, and in Danish,
while they pulled and pushed one another. This was only
the beginning of a whole series of *skaals* that boomed
out, right and left, for the next half hour. Then we
heard him ushering out the much subdued women, telling them that he was about to start cooking an eight-
course dinner "that'll take me damn near all day," he
muttered.

The Captain worked hard in the kitchen, popping
out now and again to get something from the back room.
He always returned refreshed, filled with a radiant love
for all of us. Sorry he couldn't spend more time with us,
he mentioned in passing, but it was no cinch to work on
seven different dishes "shimul . . . shimul . . . shimultanee
. . . lushly. The besht, absholutely the besht I ever made."

In fact he had to keep going back and rechecking his
"reshipes" to make sure there were no "mishtakesh."

The next time he came out it was only to inform us
that there wasn't very much in the way of lunch, but
since we were going to enjoy five separate and distinct

dishes for dinner in a few hours, it would be nice if we built up our appetites. Crackers and jam, and a large pot of coffee, helped a little to take the edge off our appetites. We weren't anxious for them to get any bigger. One of the anthropologists leaned over his coffee mug and, in a low voice, confided to me, "Captain Cleveland is behaving in a very strange way, isn't he? Almost as if he were drunk. Does he strike you that way?"

I could hardly believe that, I told him. It may be that he's nervous about having guests to dinner, which is understandable in a man who lives alone so much. At that moment the Captain entered to announce the four courses that he had decided to make for dinner: soup, fish, roast caribou, and dessert. Nobody could beat that, he said, "shpeshully shinsh I'm doing the cooking. Did I ever tell you I shailed ash a cook in the old daysh. Captains'd fight over me, my mealsh were show famush. Shtill itsh been a long time. Maybe I better take a little drop, to steady me."

An hour later he called me into the kitchen to confess that amid all the excitement of preparing such a giant meal, he had forgotten to bring the fish in from outside. Now it was too late. It couldn't possibly thaw out before tomorrow. But we'd forget all about the fish once we tasted his famous roasted caribou meat, drenched with a secret gravy from Martha's Vineyard. But it needed a bith of whisky to liven it up and give it body. He was sorry about me not being a drinker, but that's the way it was, take it or leave it. Meanwhile he'd have one quick snort and then start dinner.

We were now well into the afternoon, and could stand a bite to eat. The two doctors had received several books which kept them happy, and I went to visit some natives who shared their delicious frozen meat with me. By the time I returned, matters had grown considerably worse. The visitors had retreated into their room, seeing how Cleveland was going at that liquor. I went in search of him and was received like a king. There weren't words enough to describe his friendship for me. And to prove it he was going to whip up a special dinner of roast caribou and dessert. But would I mind giving him a hand cooking it? He was feeling a bit dizzy because he hadn't been outside for a couple of days.

Well, in the kitchen I discovered that he had not taken the caribou in either, and I had to use an ax to cut it up. Cleveland assured me that he had an oven the like of which had never been seen, and it would thaw out the meat in no time. No time at all. The hind quarter seemed to be about the right size for the four of us, so I pushed it into the oven, shoveled some coal on the fire, and in a matter of seconds the heat was going full blast, even burning some of the hairs on my bearskin pants. Cleveland went to warn the guests that dinner was under way, and that perhaps they better grab a quick nap, so they would be strong enough to withstand the great treat in store for them. On the way back he stumbled into the back room to gather some strength for himself.

Suddenly, too soon it seemed to me, I smelled burned meat. Sure enough the outer layer of the roast was fast turning to charcoal, but the inner portion was still frozen hard as granite. I decided to let the outside burn as long as the rest was edible. Cleveland had by now returned and was clamoring to start the gravy.

"You shee, I do not believe in many courshesh. Oh, I

could make them if neshashary, but I alwayssh shay, better one kind of food if itsh done right. Bad for shtomach to shtick all kindsh of shtuff into it. I'm shertainly not the man to poishon shush a friend like you. My noble Danish friend. C'mon, Peter. Lesh have one drink together." And off he went, reeling after the bottle. He came back still in one piece.

"Here we go. A big one for you, and an itty-bitty one for me. Ah yesh," he reminded himself, "you don't drink," and before I could object he downed them both.

By now Captain Cleveland was completely rudderless. He stumbled around, grumbling that nothing was in its proper "plaish," but nothing would keep him from getting on with the gravy. He was man enough for that. He poured one liquid into a pot, and then another, and somehow he even managed to drain some of the juice from the meat. The smell of burned hair and whisky spread through the house. "Thash how we do it in good old Martha's Vineyard," he said, but it sounded like *graveyard* to me. He very nearly killed any desire I ever had to visit that hallowed island.

While I kept one eye on him, with the other I suddenly saw flames shoot out of the oven. There she blows, I moaned, dumping the smoking, scorched mess into the sink, and dousing it with water. Hopefully I began to cut away the outer coal crust, and miracle of miracles, the meat underneath didn't look half bad. In fact it looked absolutely beautiful, and it tasted fine. While carving it I helped myself to a piece or two, just to "tesht" it. After all, we had a responsibility to our guests.

Well, believe it or not, we finally sat down to the table,

the four of us, and one thing was certainly true: nowhere else in the world would there ever be another roast like this one. But the Captain wasn't finished yet. "Now for shome of that gravy I promised you boysh." I followed him into the kitchen. Cleveland was oblivious of everything but his gravy. He stirred and he poured, and he spilled and he filled until finally, at long last, it was ready.

"Exshept for shome rum. Got to have shome rum."

But his strength seemed to give out as he was lugging the pot to the bottle, because the next thing I knew there was the gravy spreading all over the floor.

The disappointed faces of our two starving anthropologists appeared in a vision before me. They were going to have their gravy. I was as determined as the Captain had been. With a rag I soaked it up and squeezed the gravy back into the pot. To offset the conspicuous flavor of soap and Ajax powder, I poured in handfuls of pepper, garlic salt, whatever spices came to hand; and only when there were no more spices, did I feel that the gravy was ready. I left Cleveland asleep in the middle of the kitchen floor, where he had fallen.

At the sight of the gravy, the two men who had been sitting with roast under their noses cheered up. Patience was about to be rewarded. And when I told them that Cleveland would not be joining us, they became even happier.

The roast, it turned out, was excellent, and they helped themselves to it liberally. But it was the gravy that they really went wild about, scooping it up with teaspoons, and sopping it up with bread. Didn't I want some? No, no, I assured them. I already had my share in the kitchen. This was *all* for them. The recipe? Well, they might ask the Captain about it when he awoke.

Poor fellows, they never did get that recipe. During the night the Captain did get up, but only to call for help. He wanted one of the girls to come and undress him, and after that there were some other matters that required attention, but this would have meant going outside into the cold.

"But I'd never find it in my condition," he protested. "And besides, it would freeshe sholid."

At one stage he knocked over a box in which he kept some tame lemmings, and later, when we had all bedded down, two of them settled cozily in my beard. Cleveland must have felt their presence also, because all of a sudden he let out a roar such as I never had heard before. We lit the lamps, and there he was, his face livid with fear, squealing like a pig and staring at a few of the poor frightened rodents huddling in the corner.

"They're coming for me. Millionsh of them. Help! You gotta help!"

He got his hands on a broom and started to defend himself, smashing a pair of eyeglasses and a handsome picture of Prince Rupert, founder of the Hudson Bay Company.

This was it, I thought, as the whole house began to shake and objects of all sorts started flying around. I jumped up to put an end to the depredations of Captain Cleveland, but with my pants off and my fur coat on, I must have cut quite a figure. Anyway, everyone started laughing, including me.

The only one who did not get involved in the excitement was Fatty. She kept her head and grabbed for the only bottle left, which she stuck into her mouth and drank and drank and drank, sinking slowly to the floor like a ship settling on the bottom of the sea. There she remained as we all went back to bed, a picture of yuletide peace and contentment.

2.

Some Good Books on the Far North

WHENEVER I TRAVELED around Europe or the United States, lecturing to groups or writing for newspapers and magazines, people used to ask me what books best described life and nature in the Far North. To answer this question, I gradually compiled a list, which got longer with the passing years, experiences and reading. Then I began asking friends and fellow explorers about their favorite books, and my list got even longer. When the list of books got impossibly long, and in some respects academic, I threw it away. The following books, all published recently, are among those I have especially enjoyed.

At the head of my new list is Richard Harrington's *Face of the Arctic*. This is a cameraman's story in words, pictures, and maps of five journeys to the Canadian arctic. Everything about the book was marvelous—even the printing and binding—and I was surprised to discover that at a time when everybody expected book bargains and bought paperback editions, there was still sufficient interest in the arctic to warrant such a delightful, and expensive, volume.

Richard Harrington shows that the arctic is today undergoing a change for the better: conditions of life are becoming more pleasant and the safety and health of the people is greater. The author is not the best linguist, nor does he pretend to be a scientist or a prophet. He just takes things as he finds them and tries to capture the situation of the Eskimos at one moment in history. The result is wonderful and reads like an exciting novel.

It was evident to me that Harrington accepted the Eskimos as he respected and admired them. He was not trying to convert them or industrialize them or romanticize them, but simply aiming to tell what they were. The fact that he returned to them despite the hardships and struggles of his various trips proved this to me beyond any doubt. He describes them in suffering, in starvation, dying because they are too old to be helpful any more, trading with the white man, and taking life as it comes— and goes. He shows how they starve without complaining, because they believe that this is a part of their life. He shows how they get to know the ways of the animals, of the seasons, of the snow and the wind.

Harrington has done more than any other author I know to make the Eskimos known. He looked at things calmly and explained the "sentence of nature" in the Far North. He shows the face of the old woman to whom "life is a bigger burden than death." He also tells about numerous Eskimos in the various camps where he lived.

Science, we are told today, needs documents. Few documents will be more important than Harrington's in the years to come. I wish the author would travel to Alaska, to Greenland, and to Lapland as well and perform the same service he has for the central arctic.

Diaries are usually very tiresome to read, but the second place on my list goes to just such a book. It is strange that this book should have impressed me so much, since it deals with nothing exceptional, nothing heroic, nothing out of the ordinary. The author never intended to write a book. He just kept regular notes on what he saw and heard in his work for the Hudson Bay Company at Cape Dorset Post in Foxe Land—a place in the extreme southwestern point of Baffin Land. It is these notes which were published. I refer to John Buchan's *Hudson Bay Trader*.

This very helpful book gives a true picture of the only real difficulty in the arctic: the monotony of the place. Since the author is a keen observer, it also gives us lively anecdotes about the animals, the plants, the villages, and the trails of the Far North—facts that naturalists may well want to study in order to obtain a fuller picture of arctic life.

John Buchan, or more properly Lord Tweedsmuir, was a very well-educated man. But he never tried to act superior to the natives, to avoid the hardships or the adventures that fell to him, or even to complain about them. His book simply reports. In it the reader finds none of that false and conjured-up sentiment of sorrow or pity for the Eskimos and their way of life that mars some recent studies. Everything he writes is real, sober, and convincing.

Life at Hudson Bay Post runs along quietly. There are the trading, the walrus and seal hunts, the inland trips for foxes, hares, and ptarmigans. Snow houses must be built and the dogs cared for. All this and much more is reported with such skill by this world traveler that I some day want to have his book read to the natives in Greenland. It will give them the most accurate reflection of their own lives they have ever had.

The next book on my list of important arctic reading is *Ayorama* by Raymond de Coccola, with the collaboration of Paul King.

"Ayorama!" ("It can't be helped. That's how it goes.") This is the Eskimo philosophy of life—one which never calls in itself for progress or desires new ways. *Ayorama* deals with the central Eskimos, those around the Bathurst Inlet. But in reality it is much broader in its coverage and could be taken for an adequate description of that whole admirable people who lives where nobody else can keep alive and who have developed a culture suitable to the country.

The author is a Christian missionary and one of the rare understanding ones. Father Raymond, or "Falla" as the Eskimos call him, lived with the Eskimos for twelve years, knows the Krangmalit dialect extremely well, and traveled widely. He didn't sit in his warm hut and let the poor pagans come to him. He went out and lived with the people he wanted to convert, starved with them at times when even the well-off did not have anything to eat. In this way he won their confidence.

Most of the missionaries start by looking down on the natives and condemning their sexual customs. Not "Falla" Raymond. He just tells about what happens among the Eskimos, and gives most accurate impressions. By traveling with his friends, Falla shares their adventures in hunting bear, seal, caribou, and fish. His account of Eskimo patience is a unique achievement.

The author has some quarrels with the sorcerer Krila-lugak. He admits honestly that he does not defeat him either in discussion or by invoking miracles. He even gives the old medicine man credit for the sincerity of his faith in the traditions of his ancestors.

Mildly and patiently, Falla goes about his work and lets his example do more than his words. Unfortunately he cannot give a romantic and happy ending to his story among the Eskimos. One day an irresponsible mounted police officer came to visit the camp with an interpreter infected with influenza. This brought the disease to the whole tribe—a calamity beyond anything that ever occurred before. People died, dogs starved to death, many were sick and weak, nobody could go out hunting. This is one of the worst catastrophes I've ever heard about in the arctic—worse even than starvation and physical injury.

"Ayorama!" said the natives. Falla seems to agree: "Ayorama," he says. But many will not agree. It could be helped, they will say. The policeman should not have gone into the camp with that sick man. But just consider that everyone takes chances in the Far North; disaster is so many times just barely avoided that one is inclined to take unreasonable risks without thinking. Perhaps after all else is said, Falla is right to accept the Eskimo philosophy, to lend his help where something has gone wrong, and to leave analysis and condemnation to others. So will I.

Jeanette Mirsky's book *To the Arctic* is the next volume I would like to suggest. It became a classic as soon as it was written. No book of fiction could sound more fantastic, even though the author deals only with the facts of arctic exploration; no narrative I know of exceeds this for excitement.

Understanding is forgiveness, one is told. That is why in Miss Mirsky's clear brain and sound judgment everyone gets a fair trial, even those whose reports and opinions were hitherto judged to be absolutely incorrect. Take the erroneous reports of travel and observation given by Dr. Hayes. Miss Mirsky does not call them falsehood. She explains how the astronomer of the expedition drowned, how Hayes was not himself a navigator but was forced to do the best he could in the circumstances. As a result, his observations might well be expected to be erroneous.

Dr. Frederick A. Cook is also given plenty of attention. The author shows how it is not really accurate to call him a liar. The reports he issued about being the first to the Pole are interlaced with so many details, so many subplots and variations, that she calls him a "fiction writer" and "storyteller." She is so kind!

I do not mean to indicate that she is without critical sense or is not strong-minded. She feels, and I agree with her, that we are inclined to be too hard on the men of the past because of our fantastic accomplishments today. People who can go to the Pole and return between breakfast and dinner are inclined from the start to misunderstand the caliber of the man who trudged for months on end, hauling his sled behind him, against the forces of nature and starvation. If we could only understand their courage, we would find it within ourselves to forgive their mistakes and bad judgment. Every one of them carried one stone to the immense building that is the arctic today.

The book's introduction, written by Dr. Vilhjalmur

Stefansson, is an endorsement far beyond my own recommendation. But not even that learned doctor and great man of the arctic can be more pleased about the volume than I am.

The next volume I want to recommend is unique. Cornelius Osgood's *Winter* includes everything, omits nothing, about its subject. But it is not for that reason that I praise it so highly. What I like is that it makes the smallest details of arctic life interesting. It neither omits them as boring, nor reports them as a matter of course. It re-creates them with the full reality they have for northern travelers, makes them an adventure in themselves.

Living all alone in a small tent, then in a wooden cabin from which he can easily observe the course of the stars, the author takes what his surroundings have to offer, is brave enough to look stern reality in the face unflinchingly. He makes mistakes in adapting himself to a new life, and he admits all of them. But he learns from them. He tells us how he cuts down wood for his stove. He describes how nets are put out to catch fish for himself and his dogs.

The high spot of the book is Mr. Osgood's dealings with dogs. One must get down—or is it up?—to the business of understanding dogs in the arctic; they are frequently your only companions and you must argue with them, take their every movement for answers, speak with them about your problems and difficulties. The author does all this convincingly and without any mawkishness or embarrassment.

The book's title is defended by Osgood who says that

his home near Great Bear Lake has two seasons: Winter and August. I can agree with him about this as well as with his preference for the Eskimo sledge over the Indian toboggans or snowshoes.

No one to my knowledge has been as complete and fascinating as Osgood in his report of small details. Nor has anybody been as generous and careful in the preparation of maps and illustrations. Everything is well balanced and beautifully presented, and each time I read the book I find in it new freshness and delight.

So many books have been written about Eskimos that everybody thinks they are all known by now. But Helge Ingstad, Norwegian scientist, discovered an entirely unknown group and wrote a very fascinating book about them. It's called *Nunamiut*—the name of the people themselves. The Nunamiut never go down to the sea except for short trading trips; they spend their time in caribou hunts and fishing in the interior of Alaska, just north of the forest border in the remote mountains.

Helge Ingstad is a great scientist, undoubtedly. But he is also a very human and very interesting person from what I can see in his book. He likes people and likes to study them in their most revealing moments. Thus he tells us about the hunting customs, religious rites, and tribal practices of the Nunamiut in hearty and refreshing anecdotes rather than in scientific jargon. He gives us their humor, their sufferings and pleasures, their joys and sorrows. Through his eyes we see with understanding the human tragedies of the tribe. Even if you are not especially interested in Eskimos, you cannot help feeling sorry—or gay—over the incidents reported about the human beings studied in this book. Doctor Ingstad can give detailed information without being boring, for he knows how to get to the root of a problem quickly.

Eskimos inland are rarely heard about. They do not build snow houses but cover their tents with snow so that the heat coming from inside forms a crust protecting the dwelling from the arctic winter. They do not observe the tradition of trading wives so common among other Eskimos. But they use kayaks, not Indian canoes; and they have the same songs and stories I myself know from Hudson Bay and Greenland.

Ingstad's experiences with the Nunamiut are valuable to us. They are even more valuable to science. Beyond this, the author has added in a most splendid way to an understanding of man's ability to withstand hardships— to conquer not only the monotony of northern life but also the ferocity of the snow and the cold, the brutal out-pouring of nature's fiercest storms.

Next I should like to recommend Frank Illingworth's *Wild Life Beyond the North.* I do not remember any descriptions better than his of the animals of the arctic. Some are masterpieces—specifically, those on the lemming, the wolverine, and the reindeer.

Of course there are errors that creep into a study like this, especially since the author did not spend too much time in the Far North and had to rely on secondhand information in many cases. But even so, Mr. Illingworth has set the pace for further investigation and description. He captures poetically the appearance and spirit of each animal he deals with; and being a born storyteller, he frequently gives us word portraits of the animal in action.

These are marvelously complemented by pictures taken with skill, not to mention daring.

Constance and Harmon Helmerick's *At Home in the Arctic* is a report on a vacation and airplane trip around Alaska. But I found it to be much more. I like the spirit of these two young adventurers, so full of *joie de vivre,* so much at ease in the cabin at remote Takahula Lake. As for the skill with which the book is written, it is the best possible—it must be placed with the writings of the great narrators of the north.

Kotzebue, Point Barrow, Bathurst Inlet—these are some of the stops the airplane makes. Each punctuates some large and bold adventure which the Helmericks relate as being just "fun." But the reader knows there is more than that. The meal today is so joyful because there was nothing at all to eat yesterday. There is relaxation today because stubborn endurance and hard work have prevailed during the last two weeks. The Helmericks are interesting people, and the only reason I believe this is their best book, that they are not likely to write a better one, is because *At Home in the Arctic* is a peak achievement.

Finally, let me recommend *The Last Kings of Thule* by Jean Malaurie. I write of it last, not because it is last in place of honor on my list of good reading about the Far North, but only because I've been searching for words of praise for it. I did not know such books were written any more! Nor did I know that the kind of arctic expedition it describes was still undertaken in our times!

We hear a lot today about how scientists are taken up

north by airplane, set down in the most comfortable surroundings, given the same food and movies as the people back home have, and then picked up at an appointed hour and place. Speed and comfort are almost a religion in the arctic these days.

But along comes a man who is a great exception—a Frenchman with a lot of daring and taste for adventure as well as the utmost interest in human beings and arctic animals. He takes up the trails of old and goes to visit his "neighbors of the North Pole," stays with them in Eskimo huts, and shares their lives in long sledge journeys. Most important of all, he understands them and sympathizes with them as their equal, not as their superior. So few northern travelers take the trouble to learn the difficult Eskimo language. But Malaurie does. It is for this reason, I think, that he came to treat the Eskimos as people, not just as a little better than dogs, as is the case with many explorers who come home to tell of their experiences.

Jean Malaurie, then, is an old-style arctic explorer. With two Eskimo families he made a trip early in the spring. He had the usual but always exciting difficulties, good luck and bad. Sometimes they were starving only to enjoy food all the more when they got a walrus or a bear. After a catch, the men and dogs filled their bellies to capacity. All this time, Malaurie listened to Eskimo stories—not only the old myths, but also the events of recent years. The result is an account that is extremely valuable because it is a continuation of the earlier first-hand reports about the Thule Eskimos. It explains the development of the people after they got used to having a store where they could buy almost everything or to having American soldiers living within their district. It tells of real, modern Eskimos in the Far North.

The book contains more ethnological information about today's Polar Eskimos than I have found elsewhere. Not only are the photographs wonderful and instructive, but so are the drawings by the author of implements used for hunting. (He has also secured many of the original drawings from the Danish Count Harald Moltke.) All this, together with the author's ability to see the poetry behind the life of the Eskimo, the graceful attitude of the men and women and children, has produced a valuable book.

There are thousands of books that deal with arctic life, aspects of its nature, and great experiences in the Far North. About each of them, I'm sure, something positive can be said, something to encourage people to read them and profit from them. But from these nine volumes, I feel, can be wrested an understanding of that great and still little-known region that crowns the world as well as some insight into the men and women who live there. These books are, it seems to me, the cream of recent arctic literature. They also yield clues to the mysterious, fascinating pull the north has always had for so many of us.

This book was set in

Baskerville and Janson types by

Harry Sweetman Typesetting Corporation.

It was printed and bound at the press of

The World Publishing Company.

Design is by Larry Kamp.